INTERNATIONAL MAID OF MYSTERY

By S. Francis, H. Dugmore & Rico

David Philip Publishers
Cape Town & Johannesburg

Published 1999 in southern Africa by
David Philip Publishers (Pty) Ltd
208 Werdmuller Centre, Claremont 7708
in association with Rapid Phase (Pty) Ltd
Johannesburg

ISBN 0-86486-443-4

Reproduction by Fairstep
Printed by ABC Press, Epping, South Africa

"THE BEST IN SOUTH AFRICAN HUMOUR"
"South Africa's most successful cartoon strip
is as sharp and funny as ever."
– *The Cape Times*

"CONSISTENTLY AND HILARIOUSLY FUNNY"
"… they don't come much better than this."
– *The Daily Dispatch*

"HILARIOUS!"
"The cartoon South Africans have grown to love."
– *The Eastern Province Herald*

**"THESE TWO WOMEN HAVE CAPTURED A NEW
NICHE IN POPULAR CULTURE"**
– *The New York Times*

"PHENOMENONALLY SUCCESSFUL"
"An integral part of the South African funnybone."
– *Sawubona Magazine*

"AT LAST, IT'S TIME FOR A LAUGH"
– *Newsweek Magazine*

"MADAM & EVE FOR PRESIDENT"
"They've won the hearts of millions.
Scores high on the hilarity barometer …
fortified with liberal doses of political realism."
– *The Mail & Guardian*

**"WE LOVE THEM BECAUSE THEY
ARE OURSELVES"**
"Infectious and telling humour … the most
popular cartoon strip in South Africa."
– *The Sunday Times*

**"MADAM & EVE: TWO OF THE MOST
INFLUENTIAL SOUTH AFRICANS OF ALL TIME"**
– *Style Magazine, List of top 100 most influential people*

"MADAM & EVE – A STARTLING SUCCESS"
– *The Guardian, UK*

"CARTOON OF THE YEAR"
"Outrageously funny … with unerring humour
and intelligence."
– *Cosmopolitan Magazine*

OTHER MADAM & EVE BOOKS

The Madam & Eve Collection (1993, reprinted 1999)
Free at Last (Penguin Books, 1994)
All Aboard for the Gravy Train (Penguin Books, 1995)
Somewhere over the Rainbow Nation (Penguin Books, 1997)
Madam & Eve's Greatest Hits (Penguin Books, 1997)
Madams are from Mars, Maids are from Venus (Penguin Books, 1997)
It's a Jungle out There (David Philip, 1998)
Jamen sort kaffe er pa nu, Madam! (Gyldendal, Denmark, 1995)
Jeg giver Mandela Skylden for det her! (Gyldendal, Denmark, 1995)
Alt under kontrol i Sydafrika! (Bogfabrikken, Denmark, 1997)
Men alla dricker kaffet svart nufortiden, Madam! (Bokfabrikken, Sweden, 1998)
Madame & Eve, Enfin Libres! (Vents D'Ouest, France, 1997)
Votez Madame & Eve (Vents D'Ouest, France, 1997)
La coupe est pleine (Vents D'Ouest, France, 1998)

MADAM & EVE APPEARS REGULARLY IN:

The Mail & Guardian, The Star, The Saturday Star, City Press, The Eastern Province Herald, The Natal Mercury
The Natal Witness, The Daily Dispatch, The Cape Times, The Diamond Fields Advertiser, Die Volksblad
The Pretoria News, Zimbabwe Standard, The S.A. Times, Fair Lady, Vodaworld
Ernie (Bladkompaniet A.S., Oslo) and Larson (Atlantic Forlags AB, Stockholm)

TO CONTACT MADAM & EVE

POST: Postnet Suite # 251, Private Bag X30500, Houghton 2041, South Africa
E-MAIL: madameve@rapidphase.co.za
WORLD WIDE WEB: Visit Madam & Eve at http://www.madameve.co.za

GWEN... **WHAT ARE** YOU DOING WITH THAT FEATHER DUSTER?

WHAT DOES IT LOOK LIKE I'M DOING? I'M **CLEANING** UP!

AND NEVER MIND **ME**! WHAT ARE **YOU** DOING WITH THAT MOP AND BUCKET??

LOOK AT THIS BOOK I FOUND IN EVE'S ROOM.

"HYPNOSIS MADE EASY." ...SO??

DON'T YOU GET IT? THIS EXPLAINS **EVERYTHING**!

LIKE **WHAT**?

LIKE OUR LAPSES OF MEMORY.. OR THE FACT THAT WE UNEXPLAINABLY FIND OURSELVES DOING HOUSEWORK.

WE DO?

COULD YOU **PUT DOWN THAT IRON** WHILE I'M TALKING TO YOU?!!

OH GOOD. I SEE YOU MADE LUNCH.

I'M NOT POSITIVE, MOM... BUT I THINK EVE HAS BEEN **HYPNOTISING** US INTO DOING ALL HER WORK.

SHE HAS?

THINK ABOUT IT! YESTERDAY I WOKE UP.. AND I WAS **WASHING THE DISHES**!

YOU'RE **RIGHT**! WHEN **I** WOKE UP, I WAS HOLDING A **FEATHER DUSTER**!!

I'M TELLING YOU... SOMETHING **STRANGE** IS DEFINITELY GOING ON HERE.

I AGREE.

HEY. NO TALKING DURING MY FOOT MASSAGE!

SHHH. WE'LL DISCUSS THIS LATER.

RIGHT. MUM'S THE WORD.

5

WRITE YOUR OWN MADAM & Eve CARTOON STRIP!

IT'S EASY! IT'S FUN!

BY (YOUR NAME HERE) & RICO

EVE! IT'S AFTER FIVE O'CLOCK! WHERE'S MY _____ ?!

a) gin & tonic
b) brandy & coke
c) bar coded ID book
d) emigration papers

GIVE ME A BREAK. I WAS UP ALL NIGHT _____ !

a) waiting for armed response
b) trying to tune in to e-tv
c) applying for amnesty
d) perpetuating racial stereotypes

KNOCK! KNOCK!

WHO'S THERE?

IT'S _____

a) Dr Zuma
b) Tony Leon
c) Felicia Mabuza Suttle
d) Alan Boesak

QUICK! GET MY _____ !

a) prozac
b) prozac
c) prozac
d) prozac

HELLO! I'M COLLECTING MONEY FOR _____ .

a) the ANC
b) e-tv
c) liposuction
d) the Mpumalanga Parks Board

SLAM!

SORRY! WE ALREADY GAVE AT THE _____ !

a) office
b) traffic light
c) subliminal racists society
d) Mpumalanga Parks Board

HMPH! POLITICIANS! THEY ALL WANT THE SAME THING: _____

a) democracy
b) airline tickets
c) amnesty
d) jobs for relatives

a) MIELLLLIES!!
b) PLASTIC HANGERS!!
c) FAKE DRIVER'S LICENCES!!
d) BAR CODED ID BOOKS!!

I'LL BE RIGHT BACK! I'VE GOT A **DATE** WITH _____ !

a) destiny
b) Tony Leon
c) the Mpumalanga Parks Board
d) the African Renaissance

IN **THIS** HOUSE, IT'S A LONG WALK TO _____ .

a) freedom
b) the bathroom
c) the panic button
d) the punchline

©RAPID PHASE - 1999

HI.

...DID YOU HEAR THE ONE ABOUT PRESIDENT CLINTON?

PFRRRT!!

ARE YOU OKAY?

FINE. ER, GIN WENT DOWN THE WRONG WAY.

ANYWAY-- HOW MANY PRESIDENT CLINTONS DOES IT TAKE TO SCREW IN A LIGHTBULB?

GWEN!!

ONE. ...AND A DOZEN SECRET SERVICE AGENTS TO SPIN HIM AROUND.

HA-HA-HA

HEE-HEE-HEE! HO-HO-HO!! HAW-HAW!! HA-HA-HA

SIGH

WOW! WHY DIDN'T YOU TELL ME YOU LIKED POLITICAL JOKES SO MUCH?!

...DID YOU HEAR THE ONE ABOUT MONICA LEWINSKY?!

PFRRRT!!

MADAM & Eve

BY S. FRANCIS, H. DUGMORE & RICO

"HI MADAM."

"HI, EVE. WHAT'S FOR DINNER?"

"MEATLOAF."

"LOOK, MOTHER. THE MOON IS OUT."

"EVE, IT'S AFTER FIVE O'CLOCK AND I STILL HAVE NOT GOTTEN MY GIN & TONIC."

"YOU KNOW WHAT THEY SAY..."

"LIFE IS LIKE THE SKY."

"SOMETIMES YOU GET BLUE."

DING-DONG

"MADAM-- SOMEONE IS AT THE DOOR. I WILL GO AND ANSWER IT."

"IT'S **YOU**!! WHAT HAS HAPPENED TO YOUR FACE?!!"

"TAKE A GOOD LOOK. I HAD **PLASTIC SURGERY.**"

GASP

THIS WEEK'S EPISODE OF MADAM & EVE BROUGHT TO YOU BY THE PRODUCERS OF

Avenues

SABC

HI THERE. I COME IN PEACE.

WE TOKOLOSHES AREN'T AS BAD AS PEOPLE THINK! WE'RE VICTIMS OF MISUNDERSTANDING AND PREJUDICE! WE'RE READY TO RECONCILE WITH SOUTH AFRICANS EVERYWHERE!

PICTURE IT... A NEW RAINBOW NATION. TOKOLOSHES ... AND HUMANS ... LIVING TOGETHER IN RACIAL HARMONY.

ARE YOU CRAZY?! YOU CARRY PEOPLE AWAY AT NIGHT AND THEY'RE NEVER SEEN AGAIN!!

HEY- NOBODY'S PERFECT.

THE TOKOLOSHES WANT TO RECONCILE WITH ALL HUMANITY.

WHAT?!

SURE... WE MAY LOOK DIFFERENT FROM YOU. WE HAVE PURPLE SKIN... AND LONG, POINTY TAILS. BUT INSIDE ... WE'RE ALL THE SAME!

IF YOU PRICK US... DO WE NOT BLEED? IF YOU TICKLE US...DO WE NOT LAUGH? IF YOU POISON US...DO WE NOT DIE? TOKOLOSHES ARE PEOPLE TOO!

WHY CAN'T WE ALL JUST... GET ALONG?!

:SNIFF:

HE'S RIGHT, DAMMIT!

TOKOLOSHE TRUTH AND RECONCILIATION...

LET'S BEGIN.

OKAY. WHAT DO YOU WANT TO KNOW?

TWO YEARS AGO MY AUNT PALESA DISAPPEARED. SOME PEOPLE SAY SHE RAN AWAY WITH HER BOY- FRIEND ... OTHERS SAY SHE WAS CARRIED OFF BY TOKOLOSHES.

Bzzzt. Bzzzt. Bzzzt.

AUNT PALESA: STOCKY... BIG-BONED... WEARS GLASSES?

UH-OH.

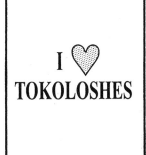

MADAM & Eve

BY S. FRANCIS, H. DUGMORE & RICO

GOOD EVENING. I WOULD LIKE TO TAKE THIS OPPORTUNITY TO APOLOGISE TO THE SOUTH AFRICAN PEOPLE FOR A RELATIONSHIP THAT WAS NOT APPROPRIATE.

IT WAS A RELATIONSHIP THAT WAS WRONG. IT CONSTITUTED A CRITICAL LAPSE OF JUDGEMENT FOR WHICH I AM SOLELY AND COMPLETELY RESPONSIBLE.

NATURALLY, I AM TALKING ABOUT THE **MIELIE LADY**... WHO I NOW REALISE I MAY HAVE TREATED UNFAIRLY.

FOR YEARS, I HAVE **SHOUTED** AT HER, **CHASED** AFTER HER, AND **SHOT** AT HER WITH THIS KATTY. ACTIONS THAT I DEEPLY REGRET.

BUT NOW IT IS TIME TO MOVE ON. I ASK YOUR FORGIVENESS... SO THAT I CAN PUT THIS BEHIND ME... AND TOGETHER WE CAN FULFILL THE PROMISE OF THE NEXT SOUTH AFRICAN CENTURY.

THANK YOU.

MIELLLIES!!

MIELLLIES!

MIELLLIES!

FORGET EVERYTHING I JUST SAID.

MIELLLIES!

MOM! YOU APOLOGISED!

FACE IT, MADAM. SHE'S NO BILL CLINTON.

©RAPID PHASE 1998

14

SOMEBODY HELP!! MY HAIR'S CAUGHT IN THE CHAIR CUSHION!

JOIN US NEXT WEEK... FOR ANOTHER EPISODE OF EMERGENCY 911.

HURRY UP! MY TV SHOW'S STARTING!

♪ GOOD MORNING! ♪

THOK!

18

MADAM & Eve

BY S.FRANCIS, H.DUGMORE & RICO

=YAWN=

MORNING, HONEY.

MORNING, GWEN.

HI. I'M GWEN ANDERSON.

YOU KNOW, PEOPLE ARE ALWAYS ASKING US... "WHERE ARE MADAM AND EVE'S MEN?... WHERE ARE ALL THE MEN IN OUR LIVES?"

THE TRUTH IS-- THEY'RE HERE... WE JUST DON'T LIKE TO SHOW THEM OFF.

MORNING EVE.

MORNING, MADAM.

YOU ALMOST READY MOM? IT'S TIME FOR OUR CARTOON.

BE RIGHT THERE. OOH... THAT'S IT, SVEN. A LITTLE TO THE RIGHT.

SEE YOU TOMORROW, SVEN.

ACH, EDITH. YOU ARE SUCH A DEVIL!

SNAP!

©RAPID PHASE-1998

SWEDES. THEY'VE GOT SUCH A DRY SENSE OF HUMOUR.

BYE GWEN!

BYE BOYS!

BYE EVE!

BYE EDITH!

SEE YOU LATER!

BYE!

SO... I GUESS WHAT WE'RE TRYING TO SAY IS...WHEN IT COMES TO MEN... DON'T WORRY ABOUT US.

...WE'RE FINE.

PHONE CALL FOR YOU. IT'S BILL CLINTON.

I'LL TAKE IT IN MY BEDROOM.

MIELLLIES!!

DON'T WORRY.
IT'S JUST MY
TAPE RECORDER.
I RECORDED
THE
MIELIE LADY.

MIELLLIES!!
MIELLLIES!!
MIELLLIES!!

SURE!
GO AHEAD—
BLAME
THE
MEDIA!

INTERVIEW FOR THE
SCHOOL NEWSPAPER...
TAKE ONE.
I'M HERE WITH MOTHER
ANDERSON. EIGHTY-YEAR-
PLUS MATRIARCH OF THE
ANDERSON FAMILY. HER
FACE, A ROAD MAP.
EACH WRINKLE TELLS
A DIFFERENT
STORY.

KNOCKING BACK
GIN & TONICS LIKE THEY'RE
GOING OUT OF STYLE,
SHE GLARES IMPERIOUSLY
FROM HER WELL-INHABITED
EASY CHAIR, SHE
FINALLY OPENS HER
MOUTH TO
SPEAK.

GO
AHEAD.
WE'RE
ROLLING.

A SIMPLE
"NO COMMENT"
WOULD'VE
SUFFICED!!

THIS IS MY COUSIN JOSEPH. HE'LL BE REPRESENTING MY INTERESTS IN OUR ANNUAL DOMESTIC WAGE INCREASE NEGOTIATIONS.

YOUR COUSIN IS A LAWYER?!

MY CLIENT FEELS SHE'S BEEN UNFAIRLY TREATED IN PREVIOUS WAGE TALKS. I'M HERE TO CHANGE THAT.

OF COURSE, IF YOU YOURSELF WISH LEGAL REPRESENTATION, I'M SURE WE CAN --

NO PROBLEM! EDITH ANDERSON-- ATTORNEY AT LAW. DON'T ANSWER ANYTHING!

HUH?

MOM! YOU CAN'T RE-PRESENT ME IN EVE'S WAGE NEGOTIATIONS! YOU'RE NOT A LAWYER!

HOW HARD CAN IT BE?! I'VE GOT A SHINY BLACK BRIEFCASE ... AND I'VE SEEN EVERY EPISODE OF "LA LAW" AND "LAW AND ORDER."

NOT TO MENTION "ALLY McBEAL".

REALLY? I LOVE THAT SHOW!

DID YOU SEE IT LAST WEEK?

WAS THAT THE ONE WITH THE DANCING BABY?

HEY!

LET'S GET STAR-TED.

RIGHT. MY CLIENT, EVE SISULU, FEELS SHE'S ENTITLED TO A MINIMUM WAGE INCREASE OF TWENTY PERCENT.

TWENTY PERCENT?!!

-CHOKE- -GASP-

MOM!! ARE YOU ALRIGHT?!!

CLUNK

SHHH. IT'S PART OF MY STRATEGY.

WILL YOU TAKE FIFTEEN?

SHE'S BLUFFING!

MADAM & EVE

BY S. FRANCIS, H. DUGMORE & RICO

MADAM & Eve

BY S. FRANCIS, H. DUGMORE & RICO

WHAT IS IT?

I NEED TO ASK YOU SOME QUESTIONS. HOW YOU ANSWER COULD IMPACT GREATLY ON MY FUTURE.

GO AHEAD.

WHAT'S A "NUMBERED SWISS ACCOUNT"?

AN UNTRACEABLE BANK ACCOUNT OVERSEAS.

IN BUSINESS, WHEN SOMEONE "KEEPS TWO SETS OF BOOKS," THAT MEANS...?

...THEY'RE USING AN ILLEGAL ACCOUNTING PROCEDURE.

WHAT'S "SKIMMING OFF THE TOP"?

HIDING UNREPORTED PROFITS.

DO PEOPLE USUALLY BUY A NEW BMW WITH A SUITCASE FULL OF CASH?

NO.

WOW.

WHAT'S THIS ALL ABOUT?

MAYBE I SHOULDN'T TAKE THAT JOB AT THE SCHOOL TUCK SHOP AFTER ALL.

WAIT! DO THEY NEED ANY SENIOR CITIZENS?

THIS IS RALPH, A FORMER SOUTH AFRICAN. I BRING HIM ALONG TO CONVINCE ALL MY PROSPECTIVE EMIGRATION CLIENTS! RALPH'S BEEN LIVING IN NEW ZEALAND FOR OVER A YEAR.

GO AHEAD, RALPH. TELL THEM HOW MUCH YOU LIKE NEW ZEALAND.

I ... I'M...

... I'M SO *BORED!!* YOU'VE GOT TO *HELP ME!!*

PLEASE. I'D KILL FOR A PIECE OF BILTONG!

RALPH! WE TALKED ABOUT THIS!

TRUST ME! AS YOUR OFFICIAL EMIGRATION CONSULTANT, MOVING TO NEW ZEALAND IS THE BEST DECISION YOU'LL EVER MAKE!

WAIT A MINUTE. IF EMIGRATING'S SO WONDERFUL -- WHAT ARE YOU STILL DOING HERE?

SHE'S RIGHT! WHAT AM I STILL DOING HERE?

MOM! WHAT ARE YOU DOING IN THE **CLOSET**?

SHHH! CLOSE THE DOOR! I'M HIDING FROM THANDI AND HER STUPID **POETRY!**

AT LAST I FOUND YOU IN THE **CUPBOARD**. HIDING THERE LIKE MOTHER **HUBBARD**.

...IN THE DARK AMONG THE **JACKETS**, WITH HATS AND COATS AND TENNIS **RACKETS**.

THANKS, GWEN. THIS IS ALL YOUR **FAULT**.

I'D TAKE THAT WITH A GRAIN OF **SALT**.

TWO CAN PLAY THIS STUPID GAME. IF YOU SAY A RHYME, I'LL DO THE SAME.

YOU DON'T HAVE TO GET **CROSS**.

IT'S NO BIG **LOSS**.

YOU'RE WALKING TOO CLOSE TO THE SWIMMING **POOL**.

WHAT DO YOU TAKE ME FOR-- A **FOOL**?

SPLASH!

YOUR HAIR'S ALL **WET** AND SO IS YOUR **HEAD**.

WHEN I GET OUT OF HERE, YOU'RE **DEAD**.

OKAY. HERE'S THE DEAL: YOU HAVE TO **STOP** THIS POETRY IF YOU CAN'T RHYME WHATEVER I SAY.

OKAY. I'LL PLAY.

BUTTERCUP.

THAT'S TOO EASY-- I NEVER GIVE **UP**.

HYDROPONICS.

YOU SURE DO LOVE YOUR GIN & **TONICS**.

I'M IN THE MIDDLE OF SOMETHING. DO YOU HAVE TO **VACUUM**?

PACUUM... TACUUM... LACUUM... UH-OH...

MADAM & EVE

BY S. FRANCIS, H. DUGMORE & RICO

CRASH!

:GASP: MOM!! ARE YOU ALL RIGHT?!

NO! I TRIPPED ON THE SLIPPERY MAIL & GUARDIAN NEWSPRINT PAPER!

THIS LOOKS LIKE A BAD CASE OF CARTOON WHIPLASH.

WE DEMAND COMPENSATION! THERE'S ONLY ONE THING TO DO!

SUE THE MAIL & GUARDIAN!

HOLD IT. YOU'RE SUING THE MAIL & GUARDIAN?!

WHY NOT? EVERYBODY ELSE IS.

AND THE FACT THAT THEY SETTLE QUICKLY HAS NOTHING TO DO WITH IT!

HELLO. I REPRESENT THE MAIL & GUARDIAN. PLEASE ACCEPT THIS GENEROUS CHEQUE IN SETTLEMENT.

WOW. THEY DO SETTLE QUICKLY.

YES! WE'RE RICH!!

OOPS.

CLUNK!

AHA! YOUR NECK SEEMS MUCH BETTER! I'LL TAKE THAT CHEQUE BACK... IF YOU DON'T MIND.

AND NEXT TIME YOU MALICIOUS, LITIGIOUS, LYING LITTLE WEASELS TRY TO SCAM THE MAIL & GUARDIAN, THINK AGAIN.

OOPS.

...SOUNDS LIKE DEFAMATION TO ME.

WE DEMAND COMPENSATION!!

I'VE BEEN READING A BOOK ON BUSINESS MANAGEMENT. FROM NOW ON, WE'RE RUNNING THIS HOUSEHOLD LIKE A REAL BUSINESS.

I'LL BE THE CEO. MOM... YOU'LL BE THE GENERAL MANAGER.

EVE... YOU'LL BE THE SENIOR VICE PRESIDENT.

REALLY?

ACTUALLY, YOU'LL BE THE TEA LADY. BUT WE NEED A LITTLE WINDOW DRESSING.

I DEMAND A COMPANY CAR.

SINCE WE'RE NOW RUNNING THIS HOUSEHOLD LIKE A REAL BUSINESS, AS CEO, I PREDICT A STRONG PERIOD OF FUTURE GROWTH.

FIRST OFF, EVE... FROM NOW ON, YOU'LL HAVE MORE RESPONSIBILITY.

IT'S ALL PART OF MY EMPLOYEE EMPOWERMENT PROGRAMME.

SO YOU'RE FINALLY EMPOWERING ME!

CHECK IT OUT. AN ELECTRIC FEATHER DUSTER.

...WITH TWO DIFFERENT POWER SETTINGS.

IF WE'RE GOING TO RUN THIS HOUSEHOLD LIKE A BUSINESS, WE'RE GOING TO NEED A CORPORATE "VISION"--ANY IDEAS?

"TO EAT MORE TAKE-AWAYS SO I DON'T HAVE TO WASH SO MANY DISHES."

"...TO TRY NOT TO RUN OUT OF GIN."

I WAS THINKING MORE LIKE..."TO BE THE MOST EFFICIENT AND SUCCESSFUL HOUSEHOLD IN ALL OF SOUTHERN AFRICA."

DOESN'T GRAB ME.

I LIKE MINE BETTER.

TO RUN THIS HOUSEHOLD LIKE A BUSINESS, CORPORATE **BUZZWORDS** ARE VERY IMPORTANT.

TODAY'S BUZZWORDS ARE... *"BENCHMARK"* AND *"INSIGHT."* LET'S PRACTICE USING THEM IN A SENTENCE.

I HAVE TO WAX THE FURNITURE. THERE'S TOO MANY **BENCHMARKS.**

I HAD THE MIELIE LADY **INSIGHT** BUT I LET HER GET AWAY.

THIS ISN'T WORKING.

THAT WAS VERY PROACTIVE.

THANKS. IT'S ALL PART OF MY **PARADIGM.**

CONGRATULATIONS, EVE. AS CEO OF THIS HOUSEHOLD, I'M PROMOTING YOU TO VICE-PRESIDENT OF *"MARKETING"* AND *"PURCHASING".*

HERE'S A SHOPPING LIST. GO TO THE SUPER-MARKET AND PURCHASE.

IN ADDITION YOU'LL BE HEADING UP TONIGHT'S FOCUS GROUP.

FOCUS GROUP?

WHILE WE WATCH, YOU TRY AND **TUNE IN** E-TV.

I DEMAND A BONUS.

MADAM & Eve

BY S. FRANCIS, H. DUGMORE & RICO

CAN I HELP YOU?

YEAH. I'M TONY... AND THIS IS VINNIE. WE REPRESENT THE PALAZZOLO FAMILY INSURANCE COMPANY.

WE'RE HERE TO MAKE YOU AN OFFER YOU CAN'T REFUSE.

YOU SELL INSURANCE?

YES. FOR A SMALL MONTHLY FEE, YOU CAN BE UNDER DON PALAZZOLO'S PROTECTION.

SORRY. WE ALREADY HAVE ARMED RESPONSE.

≡HEE-HEE≡ DID YOU HEAR THAT, VINNIE? THEY ALREADY HAVE "ARMED RESPONSE."

≡HEH-HEH≡ I HEARD.

I THINK YOU'RE MISAPPREHENDING US. WE'RE TALKING ABOUT PROTECTING YOU AGAINST HOUSEHOLD ACCIDENTS.

YEAH... LIKE YOU'RE ABOUT TO DRIVE TO THE SHOPS, WHEN-- BADDA-BING!! YOUR CAR SUDDENLY EXPLODES!

THERE'S A LOT OF THAT GOING AROUND.

SPEAKING OF CARS... IS THAT YOUR BMW PARKED OUT FRONT?

MAYBE IT IS, AND MAYBE IT ISN'T. ...WHY?

SOMEBODY'S STEALING IT.

HEY, TONY! SOME CALZONES ARE BOOSTING OUR WHEELS!!

AIN'T YOU GOT NO G*#G RESPECT?!!

HEY! COME BACK HERE?!

BLAM! BLAM!

LOOKS LIKE IT WAS A BMW THEY COULDN'T REFUSE.

IN SOUTH AFRICA, EVEN THE MAFIA NEEDS PROTECTION.

MADAM & EVE

BY S. FRANCIS, H. DUGMORE & RICO

TONY THE CHIHUAHUA & JOHNNY THE BULLFROG

- in -

"PARLIAMENTARY PROCEDURE"

BASED ON CHARACTERS CREATED BY TONY LEON & JOHNNY DE LANGE

ARF! ARF! HEY JOHNNY! LOOK! THAT CHICKEN IS CROSSING THE ROAD AGAIN!

AW, QUIT YOUR YAPPIN! ≈RIBBIT≈ I SEE HIM.

MAYBE WE COULD CROSS THE ROAD IF WE WORKED TOGETHER, HUH, JOHNNY?

≈RIBBIT≈ YOU AND ME... WORK TOGETHER?

WE BETTER BE CAREFUL THOUGH. THE ANC HAVE YET TO COME UP WITH A COHERENT ROAD SAFETY POLICY. ≈YAP YAP≈

EASY FOR YOU TO SAY! YOU'RE JUST A REACTIONARY MOUTHPIECE FOR A LIBERAL MICKEY MOUSE POLITICAL PARTY

WHAT DID YOU SAY?! ≈GRRRRR≈

YOU HEARD ME, PIPSQUEAK! ≈RIBBIT≈

TAKE THAT! POW! STUPID BULLFROG! SLAP! G∆#G CHIHUAHUA!

VROOOM!! ≈ULP≈

SQUISH!

©DAVID PHASE-1999

I DON'T GET IT. WHAT'S THE MORAL?

WHO CARES?

AS CEO OF THIS HOUSEHOLD, I'LL BE EVALUATING EVERYONE'S JOB PERFORMANCE.

LET'S START WITH YOU, MOM. WHAT EXACTLY ARE YOUR DUTIES?

I'D SAY... TO DRINK GIN & TONICS AND WATCH TV.

HOW AM I DOING?

SO FAR, I'M VERY IMPRESSED.

ACCORDING TO THIS BOOK ON BUSINESS MANAGEMENT, ...A RELAXED, "FUN" ATMOSPHERE IN THE WORKPLACE IS VERY IMPORTANT. HERE'S A PARTY HAT AND NOISEMAKER. USE THEM WHEN YOU VACUUM.

-TWEET-

THANKS. THIS REALLY HITS THE SPOT.

HOW COME SHE GETS TO HAVE ALL THE FUN?

ATTENTION EVERYONE!

AS YOU CAN SEE, I'VE MADE A HOUSEHOLD "SUGGESTION BOX."

ALTHOUGH IT'S UNLIKELY, I CAN'T RULE OUT THE POSSIBILITY THAT ONE OF YOU JUST MIGHT COME UP WITH A GOOD IDEA.

LET'S SEE... WHERE DO YOU THINK I SHOULD STICK IT?

I HAVE A SUGGESTION REGARDING THAT.

38

MADAM & EVE

BY S. FRANCIS, H. DUGMORE & RICO

HI. I'M SORRY TO BOTHER YOU. I'M HERE ON BEHALF OF THE BRAND NEW LOUIS LUYT POLITICAL PARTY!

COULD YOU AT LEAST GIVE ME A CHANCE?!!

SLAM!!

THANK YOU.

YOU'VE GOT ONE MINUTE. TELL US **WHY** ON EARTH WE SHOULD SUPPORT THE "LOUIS LUYT PARTY."

WE BELIEVE THAT THE ANC HAS DROPPED THE BALL AND MOVED THE GOALPOSTS! SOUTH AFRICA HAS BEEN **MAULED** BY CORRUPTION! WHY SHOULD THE VOTERS BE **PENALISED**? IT'S TIME TO CRY FOUL!!

WITH A LITTLE TEAMWORK, THE LOUIS LUYT PARTY PROMISES TO **SCRUM DOWN** ON CRIME AND PUT THIS COUNTRY ON THE INTERNATIONAL SCOREBOARD!

AND REMEMBER -- A VOTE FOR LOUIS LUYT... IS A VOTE FOR HIS **ENTIRE FAMILY**!!

SUPPORT **US**... I GUARANTEE THAT WITH THE RIGHT FIELD POSITIONING WE'LL BE ABLE TO SUCCESSFULLY **DROP KICK** SOUTH AFRICA INTO THE NEXT MILLENIUM!

SLAM!!

WELL? HOW'D IT GO?

SORRY, MISTER LUYT. NO ONE WANTS TO PLAY BALL.

©RAPID PHASE · 1998

40

MADAM & EVE

BY S. FRANCIS, H. DUGMORE & RICO

I'M DOING A SCHOOL PROJECT ON "TOBACCO PRODUCTS": MIND IF I ASK YOU A FEW QUESTIONS?

LIKE WHAT?

QUESTION Nº 1: ARE YOU NOW...OR HAVE YOU EVER BEEN A SMOKER?

WELL, SOMETIMES I'VE BEEN KNOWN TO SMOKE A CIGAR.

VERY INTERESTING. "...RESPONDENT FREELY ADMITS SMOKING."

QUESTION Nº 2: DO YOU HAVE ANY FRIENDS WHO SMOKE AND IF SO, WHAT ARE THEIR NAMES AND ADDRESSES?

LET'S SEE, THERE'S... WAIT A MINUTE-- YOU WANT ME TO NAME NAMES?!

WHY? YOU HAVE A PROBLEM WITH THAT?!

LET'S MOVE ON TO QUESTION Nº 3: A GENUINE COHIBA CIGAR FROM HAVANA. WANT IT?

WELL... IF YOU'RE SURE...

HA HA!! THAT WAS A TEST! YOU JUST FAILED!

I'LL HAVE TO PUT THIS IN MY OFFICIAL REPORT.

HOLD IT! ARE YOU SURE THIS IS A SCHOOL PROJECT?!

OKAY, I LIED. I SIGNED UP FOR THE ANTI-SMOKING BRIGADE.

ANTI-SMOKING BRIGADE?

WE CALL OURSELVES... "THE ZUMA YOUTH."

"ZUMA YOUTH"??

WAIT TILL YOU SEE THE COOL UNIFORMS WE'RE GETTING.

GWEN!!

41

WHERE'S EVE? THE HALLOWEEN PARTY'S STARTING IN HALF AN HOUR. SHE'S BEEN IN HER ROOM ALL DAY WORKING ON HER COSTUME.

GET READY! I'M COMING OUT!

HEE-HEE.

WHAT'S SO FUNNY?!

EVE??!!

IT'S MY HALLOWEEN COSTUME. ...LIKE IT?

HEE-HEE YOU AND THANDI MADE THAT?! I LOVE IT!

HAHAHA! HO HO HO! HAW! HAW!

VERY FUNNY, EVE.

THANK YOU.

AND DON'T WORRY. WE DIDN'T FORGET YOUR HALLOWEEN COSTUMES. THEY'RE RIGHT HERE IN THESE BOXES.

LET'S GO TRY THEM ON.

VERY FUNNY, EVE!

THIS IS GOING TO BE ONE BIZARRE HALLOWEEN.

42

43

AND IN OTHER NEWS, PRESIDENT MANDELA AND THE COUNTRY'S TOP DECISION-MAKERS MET THIS WEEK TO DISCUSS THE MORAL RENEWAL OF THE NATION.

THE THEME OF THE "MORAL SUMMIT" WAS TO "BE GOOD"... AND TO "DO GOOD."

THE EVENT WAS MARRED, HOWEVER, WHEN MANY OF THE DELEGATES BROUGHT THEIR ENTIRE FAMILIES TO TAKE ADVANTAGE OF THE FREE BUFFET DINNER.

IN ADDITION, THE SUMMIT ORGANISERS REQUEST THAT WHOEVER STOLE THE SILVERWARE AND MICROPHONES, PLEASE RETURN THEM, NO QUESTIONS ASKED.

AND NOW, WE RETURN WITH MORE LIVE COVERAGE FROM THE HISTORIC SOUTH AFRICAN MORAL SUMMIT.

MINISTER... WOULD YOU SAY THE SUMMIT HAS BEEN A SUCCESS?

DEFINITELY. I PREDICT A STRONG MORAL UPSWING IN THIS COUNTRY.

WHAT'S THAT YOU'RE HOLDING?

A TABLE CENTREPIECE. WHY? YOU GOT A PROBLEM WITH THAT?!

WAIT A MINUTE. ARE THOSE PRAWNS IN YOUR POCKET?

I DIDN'T STEAL THEM. THE BUFFET'S FREE, OKAY?!

PRESIDENT MANDELA? ...PRESIDENT CLINTON'S CALLING FROM THE WHITE HOUSE.

THANK YOU.

BILL?

NELSON! I HEARD ABOUT THAT "IMMORAL SUMMIT" YOU'RE HAVING IN SOUTH AFRICA! ANY CHANCE I CAN GET TWO TICKETS?

MORAL SUMMIT, BILL. IT'S A MORAL SUMMIT.

DARN. HOLD ON A SECOND.

BETTY -- CANCEL AIRFORCE ONE. IT'S A MORAL SUMMIT.

THE NEW INTERN'S GOING TO BE VERY DISAPPOINTED.

MIELLLIES!!

GO AHEAD! SHOOT HER WITH THE KATTY!

NO! REMEMBER THE MORAL SUMMIT! ...BE GOOD!

MIELLLIES!

OKAY. A LITTLE TO THE RIGHT.

SHHHH! I'M AIMING!

TOMORROW IS "CAREER DAY" AT MY SCHOOL. I TOLD THE CLASS YOU'D COME IN AND TALK TO THEM ABOUT YOUR CAREER.

WHAT CAREER?

... BEING A MADAM, LOTS OF US WANT TO BE ONE WHEN WE GROW UP... BUT WE DON'T KNOW HOW TO GO ABOUT IT.

JUST THINK. THE NEXT GENERATION OF SOUTH AFRICAN MADAMS ARE LOOKING TO YOU FOR INSPIRATION.

I'M SO FLATTERED I CAN'T BELIEVE IT.

WILL YOU BE NEEDING ANY PROPS? GIN & TONICS... TV REMOTE CONTROLS... CELLPHONES...?

SINCE TODAY IS "CAREER DAY" AT OUR SCHOOL, I'VE INVITED **EDITH ANDERSON** TO TALK TO US ABOUT WHAT IT MEANS TO BE A **MADAM**.

THANK YOU, THANDI. CAN WE HAVE THE FIRST SLIDE, PLEASE?

CLICK WHIRR

MADAMS in South Africa

A Career With A Future

EVER SINCE THE DAWN OF MAN, HOUSEWORK HAS ALWAYS BEEN A PROBLEM...

WOW. SHE REALLY PUT A LOT OF EFFORT INTO THIS.

CAREER DAY AT THANDI'S SCHOOL...

OKAY CLASS. WHO WANTS TO BE A MADAM WHEN THEY GROW UP?

ME!!

VERY GOOD. AND WHAT'S THE **MOST IMPORTANT** THING ALL GOOD MADAMS SHOULD HAVE?

A DOMESTIC WORKER!!

ACTUALLY, I WAS REFERRING TO "DEDICATION."

THAT WAS A TOUGH ONE.

CAREER DAY AT THANDI'S SCHOOL...

REMEMBER, CLASS... GROWING UP TO BE A MADAM ISN'T EASY. IN FACT, WHAT'S THE ONE THING ALL GOOD MADAMS HAVE IN COMMON?

I'LL GIVE YOU A HINT: IT STARTS WITH A "C".

CELLPHONES!

CREDIT CARDS!

CONTROLS FOR THE TELEVISION!

HOW DO YOU SPELL "GIN & TONICS"?

CONFIDENCE! I'M TALKING ABOUT CONFIDENCE!

I WANT A RAISE.

ABSOLUTELY NOT! MAYBE NEXT MONTH... BUT ONLY IF YOU WORK LONGER HOURS!

OKAY. THAT SOUNDS FAIR.

I'M GLAD YOU AGREE.

YOU SEE, CLASS? IF YOU WANT TO BE A GOOD MADAM, THAT'S HOW TO HANDLE A WAGE NEGOTIATION. ...ANY QUESTIONS?

YES. WHEN DO I GET MY FIFTY BUCKS FOR DOING THIS?

...I MEANT FROM THE CLASS.

OW! HEY! WATCH THE VACUUM!!

©RAPID PHASE - 1998

SORRY. I'M NEW AT THIS.

WHO ARE YOU?! WHERE'S EVE?!!

EVE? --OH, YOU MEAN Ms. SISULU. SHE'S OUTSIDE.

EVE'S DOMESTIC WORKER TRAINING ACADEMY

THIS IS PRECIOUS, MY NEW INTERN AND PROTEGÉ. I'VE DECIDED TO TEACH HER **EVERYTHING** I **KNOW** ABOUT DOMESTIC MAINTENANCE.

©RAPID PHASE - 1998

HERE'S YOUR CURRICULUM.

"TEA BREAKS... AND HOW TO EXTEND THEM." "WAGES... AND HOW TO INCREASE THEM".

"CHORES... AND HOW TO AVOID THEM."

WWW.MG.CO.ZA/MG/

WOW. I CAN'T BELIEVE I'M STUDYING WITH THE **GREAT** EVE SISULU!

MY REPUTATION PRECEDES ME.

PRECIOUS...AS MY NEW INTERN...I WILL PASS ON TO YOU ALL MY KNOWLEDGE OF DOMESTIC MAINTENANCE.   I'M READY Ms. SISULU.

YOU MUST FEEL VERY PROUD TO HAVE SUCH A DOMESTIC LEGEND WORKING IN YOUR HOUSE.

YES. WE'RE THRILLED.

WWW.MG.CO.ZA/MG/

Ms. SISULU... JUST THINK OF ME AS A **SPONGE**... THIRSTY FOR KNOWLEDGE.

...AND PLEASE, YOU DON'T HAVE TO CALL ME "Ms. SISULU."

©RAPID PHASE - 1998

CALL ME "GURU"... OR "TEACHER".

I'M GETTING NAUSEOUS.

MADAM & EVE

BY S. FRANCIS, H. DUGMORE & RICO

AND IN OTHER NEWS, AUTHORITIES HAVE BEEN INVESTIGATING **CORRUPT** PRISON OFFICIALS, WHO IN EXCHANGE FOR **BRIBES** HAVE BEEN ALLOWING PRISONERS TO LEAVE THE JAIL ON "WEEKEND PASSES".

HI. ANYTHING **ELSE** ON TV?

GWEN!! THERE'S SOME ESCAPED CONVICTS IN OUR HOUSE!!

UH... WE BEG TO DIFFER. TECHNICALLY, WE HAVEN'T ESCAPED.

YEAH. IT'S MORE OF A WEEKEND PASS. BUT IN THE MEANTIME...

PAR-TY! PAR-TY! PAR-TY!

BESIDES... THINGS HAVEN'T BEEN EASY IN PRISON. FIRST, THEY TOOK AWAY OUR CELLPHONE PRIVILEGES...

NOW THEY WANT TO TAKE AWAY OUR M-NET!

WELL, YOU CAN'T STAY HERE!

GIVE US A BREAK! DO YOU REALISE HOW MANY DRUGS WE HAVE TO SELL JUST TO GET ENOUGH MONEY TO BRIBE THE GUARDS TO LET US OUT?!

©RAPID PHASE - 1998

HEY GUYS! WE STOPPED BY THE VIDEO STORE! LOOK-- "ESCAPE FROM ALCATRAZ"!

THAT DOES IT! I'M CALLING THE WARDEN!

DON'T BOTHER-- WE BROUGHT HIM WITH US!

PARTY!!

THAT IS MY FAVOURITE PART! WHEN CLINT EASTWOOD DIGS OUT OF HIS CELL!

IF YOU ASK ME, WE DEFINITELY LIVE TOO CLOSE TO THE PRISON.

MADAM & EVE

BY S. FRANCIS, H. DUGMORE & RICO

SNAP! SNAP! SNAP!

THUNK!! WHOOOSH!!

©RAPID PHASE·1998

CONGRATULATIONS. NOT MANY PEOPLE GET THIS FAR.

YOU MEAN... WE'RE DONE?

NOT QUITE...

...YOU STILL HAVE TO DEFEAT **TUROK THE GIANT** IN HAND TO HAND COMBAT.

IF YOU ASK ME ... REGISTERING TO VOTE IS HARDER THAN WE THOUGHT.

YOU DISTRACT HIM, I'LL KICK HIM IN THE GROIN.

NO SMOKING

©RAPID PHASE-1998

MY TEACHER SAYS THE **YOUNGER** YOU BEGIN INVESTING, THE **MORE MONEY** YOU'LL HAVE WHEN YOU'RE OLDER.

THAT'S RIGHT.

HOW OLD WERE **YOU** WHEN YOU BEGAN INVESTING YOUR MONEY?

ABOUT **YOUR** AGE.

©RAPID PHASE - 1998

www.mg.co.za/mg/

WOW! YOU MUST BE THE **RICHEST** WOMAN IN THE WHOLE WORLD!

YOUR MANTRA IS... "WAGE INCREASE."

I'M NOT GETTING THIS AT ALL.

○○○

©RAPID PHASE -1998

TRANSCENDENTAL MEDIATION

MADAM & Eve

BY S. FRANCIS, H. DUGMORE & RICO

* DASHING THROUGH THE SHOPS --
WITH A CREDIT CARD TO PAY!
FROM MALL TO MALL WE GO!...

* TO THE TUNE OF "JINGLE BELLS"

...LAUGHING ALL THE WAY!!

HA! HA! HA!

PEOPLE PUSH AND SHOVE, TEMPERS START TO FRAY...

THEN SOMEONE WAVES A PLASTIC CARD...

...AND TROUBLES MELT AWAY!

OH JINGLE TILLS, RUN UP THOSE BILLS INTEREST RATES ARE HIGH!

YOU ARE THE MASTER OF YOUR CARD...

...YOUR LIMIT IS THE SKY!

OH, JINGLE TILLS, CASHIERS BILL ...ACCOUNTS FOR LOTS OF RANDS. FROM CLOTHES TO EXERCISE MACHINES -- TO KNIVES THAT CUT TIN CANS.

AS SEEN ON TV!

JINGLE TILLS, YOUR BUDGET'S KILLED -- YOU'VE SPENT TOO MUCH BY FAR...

AND THEN NEXT MONTH, SOME GUYS SHOW UP...

...TO REPOSSESS YOUR CAR.

ONLY 13 MORE SHOPPING DAYS LEFT.

MERRY CHRISTMAS!

MADAM & EVE'S NEW SOUTH
AFRICAN CHRISTMAS CAROLS

*WE THREE TOURISTS OF
ORIENT ARE...
WITH DOLLARS AND YEN
WE TRAVEL SO FAR.

* TO THE TUNE OF "WE THREE KINGS"

PEOPLE SMASH US, GRAB
AND STAB US...
AND HIJACK OUR RENTAL CAR.
OHHH...

S.A. IS A LOT OF FUN,
THE RAND IS WEAK,
WE LOVE THE SUN...

WE'D LOVE TO COME
BACK ANOTHER TIME.
(JUST CALL US WHEN
YOU'VE CUT THE CRIME.)

MADAM & EVE'S NEW SOUTH
AFRICAN CHRISTMAS CAROLS

* HARK, THE DUSTBIN MEN
ARE HERE --
COLLECTING MONEY
FOR THE YEAR!

* TO THE TUNE OF "HARK THE HERALD ANGELS SING"

STAY OUT OF SIGHT,
GET ON THE FLOOR...
WHATEVER YOU DO,
DON'T GET THE DOOR!

OOPS! DON'T FORGET
WHAT WE HAVE TAUGHT YOU,
NOW THE DUSTBIN MEN
HAVE CAUGHT YOU!

HARK! NO MONEY --
OH, WHAT SORROW.
BUT YOU CAN TRY
AGAIN...TOMORROW!

MADAM & Eve

BY S. FRANCIS, H. DUGMORE & RICO

YOU'VE GOT TO ADMIRE EVE'S DEDICATION. MOST DOMESTIC WORKERS WOULD HAVE LEFT BY NOW FOR THE CHRISTMAS HOLIDAYS.

RIGHT, EVE?

RIGHT, MADAM.

EVE! IT'S AFTER FIVE! WHERE'S MY GIN & TONIC?!

COMING RIGHT UP!

CLICK WHIRRR

SCREECH

CLICK CLACK CLICK

THAT WAS FAST.

IF YOU ASK ME, EVE WORKS EVEN HARDER DURING THE HOLIDAYS.

THANK YOU. JUST GIVE MY CHRISTMAS BONUS TO THANDI.

THIS IS EASY. SERVING CHRISTMAS DINNER WILL BE THE REAL CHALLENGE.

MADAM & Eve

BY S. FRANCIS, H.DUGMORE & RICO

HI EVE!

HI MADAM! HOW WAS YOUR HOLIDAY?

SOMETHING FUNNY WAS SUPPOSED TO HAPPEN JUST THEN, WASN'T IT?

FACE IT MADAM. AFTER TAKING ALL THAT TIME OFF AND THE NEWSPAPERS REPEATING OLD "CLASSIC CARTOONS"... WE'RE BOTH A LITTLE "RUSTY" WHEN IT COMES TO CARTOON HUMOUR.

IT'S LIKE RIDING A BICYCLE... IT'LL COME BACK TO US. LET'S START OVER.

GOOD IDEA.

HI EVE!

HI MADAM! HOW WAS YOUR HOLIDAY?!

UH...

IT'S MY LINE, ISN'T IT?

I THINK WE'RE IN TROUBLE HERE.

WHAT'S GOING ON?

MOM! THANK GOODNESS! WE NEED SOME COMIC RELIEF!

EVE! IT'S AFTER FIVE O'CLOCK! WHERE'S MY SCOTCH & SODA?!

YOU DON'T DRINK SCOTCH & SODA!

POTATOES!!

...ER, I MEAN

MIELLLIES!!

IT'S SO HARD TO GET BACK IN THE SWING OF THINGS AFTER A LONG HOLIDAY.

LOOK. THERE'S THAT NICE LADY OUTSIDE SELLING VEGETABLES.

YAAAH!!

MOM -- HAVE YOU SEEN MY NEW VIBRATING CELLPHONE?

NO DISHWASHING LIQUID
NO OMO
NO WORK

CAN'T YOU JUST WRITE DOWN A SHOPPING LIST LIKE EVERYBODY ELSE ?!!

DOMESTIC ZEN PHILOSOPHY

IF A MAID VACUUMS IN THE FOREST... AND THERE'S NO ONE WATCHING TV, DOES IT MAKE A SOUND?

INTERESTING.

LISTEN: THE SOUND OF ONE HAND DUSTING.

MADAM & Eve

BY S.FRANCIS, H.DUGMORE & RICO

Panel 1: HELLO, WE HAVE AN APPOINTMENT ON THE 23RD FLOOR.

Panel 2: PLEASE FILL THIS OUT AND SIGN IT.

Panel 3: NAME... ADDRESS... MEDICAL HISTORY... ... FAVOURITE COLOUR?!! / WE'RE VERY THOROUGH.

Panel 4: OKAY, HERE. / LET'S SEE... NAME: SANTA CLAUS ADDRESS: THE NORTH POLE.

Panel 5: "SANTA CLAUS"? IS THAT SUPPOSED TO BE FUNNY? / ER...

Panel 6: DO YOU KNOW HOW MANY PEOPLE COME IN HERE EVERY DAY AND WRITE DOWN PHONEY NAMES ON MY CLIPBOARD?!

Panel 7: DID YOU EVER STOP TO THINK THAT MAYBE I TAKE THIS JOB SERIOUSLY?!... AND THEN YOU PEOPLE COME IN HERE... SOOO IMPATIENT... ..TOO "BUSY" TO WRITE DOWN SOME SIMPLE INFORMATION THAT --

Panel 8: -- OH WHAT'S THE USE! / SOB

Panel 9: I... I'M SORRY! GIVE ME ANOTHER CHANCE! I'LL FILL IT OUT PROPERLY THIS TIME. / NO! CHOKE THE LIFT'S OVER THERE! SNIFF JUST LEAVE ME ALONE!

Panel 10: SOB

Panel 11: EXCUSE ME. WHERE DO I SIGN IN?

29 JAN 1995

©RICO 1999

72

MADAM & STEVE TSHWETE

BY S. FRANCIS, H. DUGMORE & RICO

EDITOR'S NOTE: EVE SISULU IS ON LEAVE. SO AS NOT TO DISAPPOINT READERS, WE HAVE SECURED A TEMPORARY REPLACEMENT.

STEVE! IT'S AFTER FIVE! WHERE'S MY GIN & TONIC?!

I CAN'T BELIEVE I AGREED TO APPEAR IN THIS LILY-WHITE CARTOON ENVIRONMENT.

THE SOUTH AFRICAN CRICKET TEAM HAS JUST BOWLED OUT THE WEST INDIES FOR ONLY 143 RUNS.

© RAPID PHASE - 1999

HEY! WHO TURNED OFF THE CRICKET?!

CLICK

I DID. CRICKET AND RUGBY ARE FRUSTRATING THE TRANSFORMATION OF SPORT AND SOUTH AFRICAN SOCIETY IN GENERAL. THE COMPLEXION MUST CHANGE!

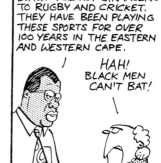

BLACKS ARE NOT STRANGERS TO RUGBY AND CRICKET. THEY HAVE BEEN PLAYING THESE SPORTS FOR OVER 100 YEARS IN THE EASTERN AND WESTERN CAPE.

HAH! BLACK MEN CAN'T BAT!

OH YEAH?! WHITE MEN CAN'T JUMP!

WANNA BET?!

OKAY -- BOWL IT TO ME RIGHT NOW.

HEY! NOT IN MY LOUNGE!!

WHACK! CRASH!

WHEN DOES EVE COME BACK AGAIN?

RUGBY. ME AGAINST YOU. THE FRONT LAWN. NOW.

YOU'RE ON.

74

MADAM & EVE

BY S. FRANCIS, H. DUGMORE & RICO

AVOID LONG ELECTION QUEUES! USED BAR CODES Only 10 Rand

YOU'RE SELLING **BAR CODES**?!

I FOUND A NICHE IN THE MARKET-PLACE. BESIDES... EVERY SA CITIZEN NEEDS A BAR CODE TO VOTE.

HEY-- THESE ARE **USED** BAR CODES!

THINGS ARE SO DISORGANISED WITH THE **IEC** RIGHT NOW, WHO'S GOING TO KNOW THE DIFFERENCE?

WILL THESE BAR CODES **WORK**?

WHY NOT? I TOOK THEM OFF **REAL** FOOD AND HOUSEHOLD PRODUCTS.

OF COURSE, YOU DON'T **HAVE** TO BUY ONE. GET YOUR BAR CODE FROM HOME AFFAIRS... GO **STAND** IN A **LONG** QUEUE, **WAITING** FOR **HOURS**...

HERE'S MY MONEY. I'LL TAKE ONE.

SMART MOVE.

ME TOO.

BY THE WAY -- WHEN YOU GO TO REGISTER, JUST REMEMBER TO SIGN YOUR NAME AS "ONE DOZEN EGGS."

AND **YOUR** NEW NAME IS "LOW-FAT YOGHURT".

A SMALL PRICE TO PAY FOR HASSLE-FREE DEMOCRACY, HEY, LOW-FAT?

THAT'S **MS. YOGHURT** TO YOU.

79

84

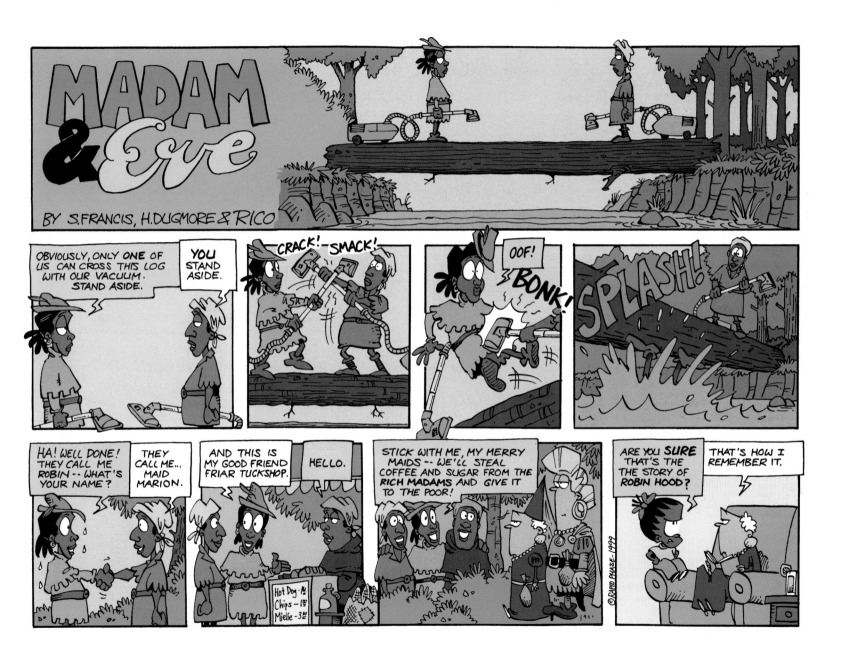

MADAM & Eve

BY S. FRANCIS, H. DUGMORE & RICO

EVERYONE--THIS IS MISS CHENG. SHE'S A MASTER OF FENG SHUI.

FENG-SHUI! HEE-YA! HOO! HOO!

FENG SHUI: THE ANCIENT ART OF ARRANGING FURNITURE AND SPACE TO OPTIMISE HARMONY AND THE FREE FLOW OF COSMIC ENERGY.

I KNEW THAT.

FOR MY FEE OF FIVE HUNDRED BUCKS, I WILL NOW WALK THROUGH YOUR HOUSE TO RECEIVE COSMIC FENG SHUI VIBRATIONS...

I'M SENSING AN AREA OF INSECURITY AND PARANOIA...

ACE ARMED RESPONSE

NOW... I'M GETTING AN AURA OF COMPLETE RELAXATION...

MIELLLIES!!

I'M PICKING UP NEGATIVE VIBRATIONS OF ANGER AND FRUSTRATION!

I HAVE SEEN ENOUGH! TO MAXIMISE HARMONY AND POSITIVE ENERGY IN YOUR HOME... YOU MUST RE-ARRANGE ALL YOUR FURNITURE EXACTLY LIKE THIS DIAGRAM.

THANK YOU, MISS CHENG. HERE'S YOUR MONEY.

WELL, MOM? WHAT DO YOU THINK?

I THINK WE JUST GOT "FENG SHUIED" OUT OF FIVE HUNDRED BUCKS!

©RAPID PHASE · 1998 · WWW.MG.CO.ZA/MG/

87

MADAM & Eve

BY S. FRANCIS, H. DUGMORE & RICO

BLINK!

AHA!! YOU BLINKED! I WIN! YOU OWE ME A RAISE!!

BOY, THESE **WAGE NEGOTIATIONS** GET **TOUGHER** EVERY YEAR.

I'LL GET THE EYE DROPS.

MADAM & Eve

BY S. FRANCIS, H. DUGMORE & RICO

I'M GOING INTO SHOW BUSINESS WHEN I GROW UP.

MY TEACHER SAYS I'M A REAL COMEDIAN.

ANSWER THIS QUESTION: WHAT **MEDICINE** DO WE GET FROM **PIGS**?

OINKMENT. GET IT?

WHAT MEDICINE DO WE GET FROM **SHEEP**?

AAAAAAASPIRIN.

THIS IS A GOOD ONE: WHAT MEDICINE DO WE GET FROM COWS? ...GIVE UP?

©RAPID PHASE - 1995

MOOOOOT! GET IT? MOOOOOOT!!

I WROTE ALL THOSE JOKES MYSELF. WANT TO HEAR **MORE**? ...KNOCK KNOCK.

WWW.MADAMEVE.CO.ZA

WHO'S THERE?

91

MADAM & Eve

BY S. FRANCIS, H. DUGMORE & RICO

DOOG GNINROM!! ...IN CASE YOU'RE WONDERING, THAT'S "GOOD MORNING" SPELLED *BACKWARDS*.

www.madameve.co.za

SHE'S FULL OF INFORMATION LIKE THAT.

HEY! TRY SPELLING "EVE" BACKWARDS! ...IT'S STILL *EVE!* YOU *CAN'T* SPELL IT BACKWARDS!

I KNOW.

...I WOULDN'T BE TOO SMUG. TRY SPELLING "MADAM" BACKWARDS.

GASP IT STILL SPELLS MADAM!

HA!! MY NAME'S EDITH. YOU CAN DEFINITELY SPELL *THAT* BACKWARDS.

©RAPID PHASE - 1999

YES, BUT I CALL YOU "MOM". AND "MOM" SPELLED BACKWARDS... IS STILL "MOM".

THIS IS **SPOOKY**.

THIS COULD BE A **BAD OMEN**. MAYBE I SHOULD TAKE THE DAY OFF BEFORE SOMETHING UNLUCKY HAPPENS.

YOU'RE RIGHT. BETTER COME BACK TOMORROW.

SREKCUS.

92

MADAM & EVE

BY S. FRANCIS, H. DUGMORE & RICO

I HEAR THE SCHOOL TUCK SHOP IS UNDER NEW MANAGEMENT.

TUCK SHOP

YOU'RE RUNNING THE SCHOOL TUCK SHOP?!!

I HEARD IT WAS AN EXCELLENT INVESTMENT OPPORTUNITY.

OKAY, I'LL HAVE A TOASTED CHEESE SANDWICH.

SORRY. TOASTED SANDWICHES ARE LOW PROFIT ITEMS. HOW ABOUT A NICE GOOEY CHOCOLATE BAR?

HOW MUCH?

EIGHT BUCKS.

EIGHT BUCKS FOR A CHOCOLATE BAR?!

IT'S MY NEW PRICE STRUCTURE. I HAVE LOTS OF OVERHEADS.

HOW ABOUT A BAG OF JELLY BEANS? THE DENTIST DOWN THE STREET GIVES ME A KICKBACK.

WHAT'S NEXT? SELLING GIN & TONICS?!

ACTUALLY... THAT'S NOT A BAD IDEA.

DON'T YOU HAVE ANY PRINCIPLES?!!

DON'T MENTION PRINCIPALS. I HAD TO PAY YOUR SCHOOL PRINCIPAL JUST TO GET THIS CONCESSION.

I'LL BE BACK.

NOTHING LIKE A LITTLE HEALTHY COMPETITION FOR A GOOD BUSINESS ENVIRONMENT.

HONEST THANDI'S TUCK SHOP

MADAM & Eve

BY S. FRANCIS, H. DUGMORE & RICO

OKAY, EVERYONE. FOLLOW ME AND STAY CLOSE.

I GIVE YOU... MOTHER ANDERSON IN HER NATURAL HABITAT.

GASP

WOW

OOOH.

OVER HERE... YOU CAN STILL SEE THE EMPTY GIN & TONIC GLASSES.

AND LOOK! THE KATTY SHE USED TO CHASE THE MIELIE LADY... ONLY AN HOUR AGO!

COOL!

GASP

COULD I... TOUCH HER?

IT COULD BE DANGEROUS. I'LL HAVE TO CHARGE YOU EXTRA.

OKAY. GO AHEAD.

CHOKE

WHO'S THERE?!!

AAAAH!!

BE SURE TO TELL YOUR FRIENDS! TUESDAYS IS HALF-PRICE DAY!

"MADAMS FROM HELL"... A WALKING TOUR?

JUST DOING MY BIT TO PROMOTE TOURISM.

WOULDN'T THEY RATHER SEE THE BIG FIVE?

FRANKLY, YOU'RE A LOT SCARIER.

SOUTH AFRICAN CONSULATE, INDIA...

SAY HELLO, KID. I'M THE NEW CONSUL GENERAL.

...ARE YOU MR. VASSEN?

MR. VASSEN HAD A SLIGHT PUBLIC RELATIONS PROBLEM. I'M TAKING HIS PLACE.

SAY, AREN'T YOU THE GUY WHO DID...

SARAFINA 2. BUT... SHH! I'M TRYING TO KEEP A LOW PROFILE.

YOU CAN COUNT ON ME, SIR.

WUPWUPWUPWUP

BY THE WAY... I HIRED A HELICOPTER. WANT TO GO FOR A SPIN?

SHOULDN'T YOU SEE YOUR OFFICE FIRST, SIR?

SOUTH AFRICAN CONSULATE, INDIA...

WHAT'S WRONG, KID?

TO BE CANDID, SIR... I CAN'T BELIEVE THEY MADE YOU CONSUL-GENERAL ...ESPECIALLY AFTER THE SARAFINA 2 SCANDAL.

NOTHING WAS EVER PROVEN! ...BESIDES... THE SOUTH AFRICAN GOVERNMENT BELIEVES IN GIVING PEOPLE A SECOND CHANCE!

AND IF IT'S ANY CONSOLATION, I DIDN'T EVEN WANT TO BE POSTED TO INDIA!

WHAT CONSUL-GENERALSHIP DID YOU WANT, SIR?

SWITZERLAND! BUT THEY'RE KEEPING THAT ONE FOR COLIN CHAUKE!

OUCH, SIR.

SOUTH AFRICAN CONSULATE, INDIA...

CONGRATULATIONS ON BEING APPOINTED CONSUL-GENERAL TO INDIA, SIR.

THANKS, KID.

AND JUST BECAUSE I'M THE PRODUCER OF SARAFINA 2, DON'T THINK I'M GOING TO KICK BACK AND TAKE IT EASY!

YOU'RE GOING TO SEE SOME BIG CHANGES! A TOTAL RESTRUCTURING!

...OF FOREIGN POLICY?

...OF MY OFFICE! MAKE A NOTE. WE'LL PUT THE RECORDING STUDIO HERE.

UH, SIR? ACCORDING TO YOUR BLUEPRINTS, THAT'S WHERE THE SAUNA AND JACUZZI GO.

SOUTH AFRICAN CONSULATE, INDIA...

KID -- I WANT YOU TO ORGANISE A HUGE PARTY TO CELEBRATE MY POSTING AS CONSUL-GENERAL SPARE NO EXPENSE!

BUT SIR...

... GIVEN THAT YOU'RE THE FORMER PRODUCER OF **SARAFINA 2** ... WON'T YOU BE CRITICISED FOR SPENDING MORE TAXPAYER'S MONEY?

GOOD POINT! WE'LL JUSTIFY THE EXPENSE BY MAKING IT A PARTY AND A LIVE MUSICAL WITH EDUCATIONAL MESSAGES FOR THE PEOPLE OF INDIA.

"EDUCATIONAL MESSAGES," SIR?

DAMMIT, MAN -- DO YOU HAVE ANY IDEA HOW MANY PEOPLE IN INDIA DON'T KNOW THE PROPER WAY TO **EAT CAVIAR?!!**

GREAT PARTY, MISTER CONSUL-GENERAL.

THANKS, KID.

THIS MUST HAVE COST THE TAXPAYERS **MILLIONS**.

I TOLD YOU, KID. IT'S A **JUSTIFIED** EXPENSE BECAUSE, LIKE IN **SARAFINA 2**, THERE'S AN **EDUCATIONAL MESSAGE!**

WHAT EDUCATIONAL MESSAGE IS THAT, SIR?

ALWAYS BE CAREFUL WHO YOU APPOINT TO A DIPLOMATIC POST.

DO YOU THINK THE GOVERNMENT WILL **GET** THE MESSAGE?

BITE YOUR TONGUE, KID. WHOAH!! WE NEED MORE **DOM PERIGNON!**

©RAPID PHASE - 1999   WWW.RAPID.CO.ZA/MG/

YES! I JUST LANDED ON ELOFF STREET IN DOWNTOWN JOHANNESBURG -- THE MOST VALUABLE PROPERTY IN MONOPOLY!

SOMEONE REALLY SHOULD UPDATE THIS GAME.

HA! YOU LANDED ON ELOFF STREET! I OWN FOUR HOTELS!

GOOD THING I PAY NO RENT SINCE WE'RE RELATED.

OKAY. I PASSED "GO". GIVE ME MY TWO MILLION BUCKS KICKBACK.

DARN. I LANDED IN JAIL FOR CORRUPTION. LUCKILY, I HAVE 17 "GET OUT OF JAIL FREE" CARDS.

WAIT A MINUTE! WHAT KIND OF CRAZY GAME IS THIS?

ANC MONOPOLY.

WHAT'S THE MATTER, EVE? DON'T YOU LIKE OUR NEW GAME?

WE CALL IT... ANC MONOPOLY.

GO AHEAD. PICK UP A "COMMUNITY CHEST" CARD AND READ IT.

I CAN'T. IT'S BLANK.

I KNOW! THERE'S NOTHING LEFT IN THE COMMUNITY CHEST!

≷ HEE-HEE ≷ IT'S ALL BEEN EMBEZZLED! GET IT?! HAHAHA!!

≷ HEE-HEE ≷ I LOVE THIS GAME.

MADAM & EVE

BY S. FRANCIS, H. DUGMORE & RICO

I HOPE THIS GAME RESERVE IS GOOD. I'VE HEARD RUMOURS THAT THINGS HAVE BEEN GOING *DOWNHILL*.

NO WORK NO FOOD NO MONEY

BE SURE TO KEEP YOUR WINDOWS ROLLED UP.

BECAUSE OF THE ANIMALS?

BECAUSE WE DON'T WANT ANY PAMPHLETS, FLOWERS OR PLASTIC HANGARS.

PSSST. HEY! YOU WANT TO SEE THE *BIG FIVE*? ONLY FIFTY BUCKS. ...EACH.

HERE. ...AND THIS BETTER BE GOOD.

COME ON OUT GUYS - WE GOT A CUSTOMER!

WAIT A MINUTE! A WARTHOG, A VULTURE, AN AARDVARK, A WILDEBEEST AND A HYENA?!! THAT'S NOT THE BIG FIVE!!

I WANT MY MONEY BACK.

HEE HEE. HEAR THAT? SHE WANTS HER MONEY BACK.

UH, MADAM... SOME ANIMALS STOLE OUR TYRES.

--HEY!! WHAT HAPPENED TO MY CAMERA?!

THE MONKEY TOOK IT.

MPUMALANGA PARKS BOARD

MADAM & EVE PRESENT:

The Madam of Venice

BY S. FRANCIS, H. DUGMORE & RICO

TO CLEAN... OR NOT TO CLEAN. THAT IS THE QUESTION.

CRASH!!

HARK! WHAT VASE FROM YONDER TABLE BREAKS?

ONCE MORE INTO THE BREACH, DEAR FRIENDS, ONCE MORE.

OUT DAMNED SPOT! OUT, I SAY!

SISULU! SISULU! WHEREFORE ART THOU SISULU?!

ªSIGHª IS THIS A FEATHER DUSTER I SEE BEFORE ME?

HOW IS IT THAT THE CLOUDS STILL HANG ON YOU?

SINCE BREVITY IS THE SOUL OF WIT, I WILL BE BRIEF.

OH WHAT A ROGUE AND PEASANT SLAVE AM I!!

A RAISE! A RAISE! MY KINGDOM FOR A RAISE!

THE LADY DOTH PROTEST TOO MUCH, METHINKS.

SOMETHING IS ROTTEN IN THE STATE OF DENMARK.

I AM A MAID. IF YOU PRICK US, DO WE NOT BLEED? IF YOU TICKLE US... DO WE NOT LAUGH??

THIS IS BEING LAID ON WITH A TROWEL.

HERE. TAKE MY RICHES. AND NOT A PENNY MORE.

MADAM. YOU ARE FULL OF THE MILK OF HUMAN KINDNESS?

HMPH. MUCH ADO ABOUT NOTHING.

WHAT A PIECE OF WORK IS A MAID.

ALL'S WELL THAT ENDS WELL.

©RICO/MASE 1999

WHAT'S THAT?

IT'S MY NEW INVENTION. A "SUBLIMINAL RACISM DETECTOR."

WHENEVER SOMEONE SAYS SOMETHING THAT CAN BE CONSTRUED AS "SUBLIMINALLY RACIST", IT BEEPS.

GO AHEAD. TRY IT OUT.

OKAY. BUT REMEMBER... NOT EVERYTHING'S BLACK OR WHITE.

BEEP
BEEP
BEEP
BEEP
BEEP

WHAT'S WITH THE FUNNY MACHINE?

IT'S A NEW INVENTION. ..."A SUBLIMINAL RACIST DETECTOR."

WHERE'D YOU GET IT?

EVE **MADE** IT.

BEEP
BEEP
BEEP
BEEP
BEEP

SORRY. THE WORD "MAID" IS SUBLIMINALLY RACIST.

I'M USING IT AS A VERB!!

HOW'S EVE'S SUBLIMINAL RACISM DETECTOR?

IT ACTUALLY SEEMS TO WORK.

OH, EVE. COULD I PLEASE HAVE SOME COFFEE?

OKAY.

...AND MAKE SURE IT'S DECAFFEINATED.

BEEP
BEEP
BEEP
BEEP

HMMM. IT STILL NEEDS A LITTLE FINE TUNING.

"BLACKMAIL."

"NIGGARDLY."

"GAFFER."

GIVE UP, MADAM. THERE'S NO WAY YOU CAN **FOOL** MY SUBLIMINAL RACISM DETECTOR.

BY THE WAY... WHICH KEY OPENS YOUR BEDROOM CLOSET?

THE COLOURED KEY.

BEEP BEEP BEEP BEEP BEEP

HEE-HEE.

DO YOU SMELL SMOKE?

EVE! WHAT HAPPENED?!

IT'S MY SUBLIMINAL RACISM DETECTOR.

I TOOK IT TO **PARLIAMENT** TO TEST IT OUT.

... SO?

IT OVERHEATED.

108

FUTURE YIZO YIZO TV PROGRAMMES

— o —

THE BOLD & THE YIZO YIZO...

OH JOHN, JOHN. I'M IN LOVE WITH YOU.

GIVE ME YOUR LUNCH MONEY OR I'LL SHOOT YOU.

SUBURBAN YIZO YIZO...

BLAM! BLAM! BLAM! BLAM!

BLAM! BLAM! BLAM! BLAM!

FELICIA YIZO YIZO...

LET'S SEE WHAT OUR STUDIO AUDIENCE THINKS!

CLICK!

CLICK!

CLKK!

TUNE IN NEXT WEEK FOR ANOTHER EPISODE "YIZO YIZO".

COME ON. LET'S GO.

WHERE ARE WE GOING?

TO YOUR SCHOOL. I WANT TO SEE FOR MYSELF HOW THIS YIZO YIZO TV PROGRAMME HAS AFFECTED EDUCATION.

YO MAMA! GIVE UP SOME G#¤# MONEY... OR YOU MIGHT FIND YOUR HEAD IN THE SINK!

WAS THAT ONE OF THE BULLIES?

NO. THAT WAS MY HISTORY TEACHER.

MADAM & Eve

BY S. FRANCIS, H. DUGMORE & RICO

Panel 1: YOU WANTED TO SEE ME, MISTER PRESIDENT? / YES THABO. AS MY HEIR APPARENT, IT'S TIME FOR ME TO PASS ON ALL MY SECRETS.

Panel 2: YOU MEAN...? / YES! FROM *MADIBA* MAGIC... TO *MBEKI* MAGIC!

Panel 3: I'M HONOURED, SIR. WHAT'S FIRST? / I THOUGHT WE'D BEGIN WITH THE FAMOUS "SAWING A WOMAN IN HALF" TRICK.

Panel 4: LUCKILY, DOCTOR ZUMA HAS GRACIOUSLY AGREED TO VOLUNTEER. / HI DOCTOR ZUMA. / HELLO, THABO.

Panel 5: OKAY-- NOW TAKE THIS SAW AND SAY... "MBEKI MAGIC"! / MBEKI MAGIC!!

Panel 6: ARE YOU **SURE** THIS WILL WORK, MISTER PRESIDENT? / DON'T WORRY-- SHE'S PRACTICALLY INDESTRUCTIBLE.

Panel 7: SAW SAW SAW SAW SAW

Panel 8: CONGRATULATIONS THABO! YOU DID IT! LET'S HAVE A BIG HAND FOR DOCTOR ZUMA! / THANK YOU, MISTER PRESIDENT. THIS **MBEKI MAGIC** IS EASIER THAN I THOUGHT. / CLAP CLAP CLAP CLAP CLAP CLAP CLAP CLAP

Panel 9: AND NOW, FOR OUR NEXT TRICK... THE DISAPPEARANCE OF **TONY LEON!**

Panel 10: REALLY?! YOU **KNOW** THAT ONE? / I WISH.

MADAM & Eve

BY S. FRANCIS, H. DUGMORE & RICO

AND THE WINNER FOR THE BEST DOMESTC WORKER IN A SUPPORTING ROLE IS...

Precious Ndlovu

Rose Ntini

Elizabeth Mohale

Eve Sisulu

EVE SISULU!!

CLAP CLAP CLAP CLAP CLAP CLAP

:GASP: I--I--CAN'T BELIEVE IT!!

CLAP CLAP CLAP CLAP CLAP

I...I'M SO SURPRISED... I DIDN'T EXPECT TO WIN. I'D ...LIKE TO THANK THE ACADEMY OF DOMESTIC WORKERS...

AND THERE ARE SO MANY PEOPLE TO THANK--WITHOUT WHOSE SUPPORT--I WOULDN'T BE HERE TONIGHT. MOTHER ANDERSON AND HER GIN & TONICS; LITTLE THANDI, ERIC AND LIZEKA; THE MIELIE LADY...

BUT MOST OF ALL, I'D LIKE TO THANK THE **ONE PERSON** WHO STOOD BEHIND ME AND SUPPORTED ME FROM THE BEGINNING...

:CHOKE: I'M TALKING ABOUT MY MADAM **GWEN ANDERSON** --WHO HAS GENEROUSLY AGREED TO **DOUBLE** MY MINIMUM WAGE!!

©RAPID PHASE-1999

:SNIFF: **THIS IS FOR YOU, GWEN!!**

CLAP CLAP CLAP CLAP CLAP CLAP CLAP CLAP CLAP

WAIT A MINUTE. YOU AGREED TO **DOUBLE** HER MINIMUM WAGE?

NO. BUT I'M **GOING** TO.

I NEVER REALISED UNTIL THIS MOMENT JUST HOW MUCH AFFECTION EVE TRULY FEELS ABOUT ME...

EAT YOUR HEART OUT GWYNETH PALTROW.

Panel 1:
WHAT'S THAT EVE?

AN ANTIQUE SCRAPBOOK. IT'S A HISTORY OF ALL MY ANCESTORS.

Panel 2:
BELIEVE IT OR NOT, MY GREAT GREAT GREAT GREAT GREAT AUNT ACTUALLY WORKED FOR WILLIAM SHAKESPEARE.

Panel 3:
YOU'RE KIDDING.

NOT AT ALL. AS A MATTER OF FACT, SHE OFTEN HELPED HIM WITH MANY OF HIS FAMOUS PLAYS.

Panel 4:
I THINK I'VE GOT IT! "A MIDSUMMER'S NIGHT TEAM?" ...CREAM? ...SHEBEEN?

I'D GO WITH "DREAM." IT HAS A NICE RING TO IT.

Panel 5:
SHAKESPEARE & EVE

THESE ARE MY DOGS. PLEASE MAKE SURE THEY ARE FED EVERY DAY.

I'LL SEE TO IT RIGHT AWAY.

Panel 6:
WHAT ARE THEIR NAMES?

NAMES?! WHY, I NEVER THOUGHT OF CALLING DOGS A "NAME".

Panel 7:
...ANY SUGGESTIONS?

HOW ABOUT... "ROMEO"... AND "JULIET"?

Panel 8:
CATCHY TITLE.

COME ON BOY! DINNER'S READY! ROMEO... ROMEO... WHEREFORE ART THOU, ROMEO?!

Panel 9:
SHAKESPEARE & EVE

EVE ...YOU REMEMBER MY MOTHER, EDITH SHAKESPEARE. SHE'LL BE STAYING WITH US FOR A FEW DAYS.

Panel 10:
WELL, I'LL LEAVE YOU TWO ALONE. I'M SURE YOU TWO HAVE A LOT TO TALK ABOUT.

Panel 11:

Panel 12:
NOW IS THE WINTER OF OUR DISCONTENT.

A HORSE... A HORSE... MY KINGDOM FOR A HORSE!

116

SHAKESPEARE & EVE

DOUBLE DOUBLE TOIL AND TROUBLE...

FIRE BURN AND CAULDRON BUBBLE!

EYE OF NEWT AND TOE OF FROG--

WAIT A MINUTE. ARE YOU **SURE** THIS IS THE RECIPE FOR ELIZABETHAN POTJIEKOS?

TRUST ME. IT'S AN ACQUIRED TASTE.

www.madameve.co.za

SHAKESPEARE & EVE

EVE -- PLEASE DON'T LET MY MOTHER'S ANTIC DISPOSITION BOTHER YOU. ACTUALLY, SHE'S FULL OF THE MILK OF HUMAN KINDNESS.

MMM HMM.

OOPS.

HARK!! WHAT LIGHT ON YONDER WINDOW BREAKS?!

CRASH!

AND WHERE'S MY CAKE & ALE?! STOP HOB NOBBING AROUND! WHAT A PIECE OF WORK IS A MAID!

SIGH
THE TAMING OF THE SHREW.

JISLAAIK, THIS WOMAN COMES UP WITH CATCHY TITLES!!

117

FOR SCHOOL I HAVE TO WRITE DOWN WHAT I WANT TO BE WHEN I GROW UP.

MMMHMM.

I THINK I'VE FIGURED IT OUT. I WANT TO BE RICH, POWERFUL AND RECOGNISED BY MILLIONS OF PEOPLE.

HOW DO YOU SPELL "PRESIDENT"?

"P-R-E-S-I-D-E-N-T". ...GOOD CHOICE.

I'M NOT DONE YET. HOW DO YOU SPELL "INTERN"?

EVERYBODY AT SCHOOL'S TALKING ABOUT THE MILLENIUM BUG. DO YOU KNOW WHAT IT IS?

ACTUALLY... YES. IT'S THIS GIANT BUG THAT EATS YOUR HOME COMPUTER. IT'S HORRIBLE!

THAT'S WHAT I THOUGHT. BUT YOU DON'T HAVE TO WORRY! I JUST SPRAYED YOUR KEYBOARD WITH BUG SPRAY!

TWO CAN PLAY THIS GAME.

EVE!!

WHAT DO YOU THINK YOU'RE DOING?!

YOU'VE HEARD OF THE NEW "HANDS FREE" CELLPHONES?

YES. ...SO?

I'VE JUST INVENTED "HANDS FREE" IRONING

HOW FRESH IS IT? EXCUSE ME A SECOND.

WHACK! WHACK! WHACK!

I THINK I'LL PASS. NEVER LET THE CUSTOMER SEE THE KITCHEN.

THANDI'S PERFORMING AN ACT IN HER SCHOOL SHOW THIS YEAR.

REALLY? WHAT'S SHE DOING? SINGING? ...DANCING? VENTRILOQUISM.

EVE! IT'S AFTER FIVE! WHERE'S MY GIN & TONIC?!

CUTE. WHO IS THE DUMMY SUPPOSED TO BE?

FIRST OF ALL, I HAVEN'T HAD A **RAISE** IN TWO YEARS.

THEN, EVERY TIME THE COFFEE OR SUGAR GOES MISSING, THEY ALWAYS BLAME **ME**.

...AND PAID LEAVE? FORGET ABOUT IT. I'M LUCKY IF I GET **SUNDAYS** OFF. THANK YOU FOR LISTENING.

CUSTOMS NEXT TIME SOMEONE ASKS "ANYTHING TO DECLARE"... LET ME DO THE TALKING.

119

MADAM & EVE

BY S. FRANCIS, H. DUGMORE & RICO

I'M INNOCENT! DO YOU HEAR ME?! I WAS FRAMED!!

I'M INNOCENT! DO YOU HEAR ME?! I WAS FRAMED!!

DO YOU **HAVE** TO COPY EVERYTHING I SAY, MZWAKHE?!

SORRY, REVEREND. I'M NOT VERY **SLOPPY** -- I JUST LOVE TO **COPY**. I JUST LIKE TO **RHYME** ALL OF THE **TIME**.

I CAN'T BELIEVE IT -- IN ALL THE **JAIL CELLS** IN ALL THE WORLD, I HAVE TO GET **MZWAKHE MBULI** AS A CELLMATE.

REVEREND BOESAK... THAT'S A **COMPLIMENT**. CAN I OFFER YOU A **PEPPERMINT**?!

GUARD! I DEMAND A NEW CELLMATE!!

SORRY, REVEREND BOESAK. THE PAPERWORK'S ALREADY GONE THROUGH. I'M AFRAID YOU AND MZWAKHE MBULI ARE ROOM-MATES FOR THE NEXT **SIX YEARS**.

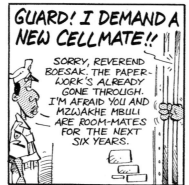

I'M BEING **TESTED!!** THAT'S IT!! THIS IS SOME SORT OF **DIVINE TEST!**

AND SINCE **MORE IS LESS**, A **TEST**... ALWAYS BRINGS OUT YOUR **BEST**.

FIFTY BUCKS SAYS THEY WON'T LAST **ONE DAY** IN THAT CELL TOGETHER.

YOU'RE ON.

MZWAKHE... AS LONG AS WE'RE **HERE** TOGETHER, LET'S MAKE THE MOST OF IT. LET US KNEEL DOWN TOGETHER AND PRAY FOR FORGIVENESS.

FORGIVENESS FOR **WHAT**, REVEREND?? REMEMBER, WE WERE **FRAMED** -- WE DIDN'T **DO** ANYTHING.

GOOD POINT.

BESIDES... KNEELING IS COOL... BUT NOT VERY **CLEAN**. MY PANTS GET ALL DIRTY AND THERE'S NO WASHING **MACHINE**...

I CAN'T TAKE THIS ANYMORE!!

HELP! THE REVEREND IS **MAD!** HE'S CHOKING MY NECK -- IT FEELS VERY **BAD!!**

HELP ME PLEASE GUARD!! I HATE TO BE **CRYING!!** I CAN'T SEEM TO BREATHE, I THINK I AM **DYING!!**

DARN. I **KNEW** I SHOULD HAVE GONE FOR A HUNDRED!

MADAM & EVE

BY S. FRANCIS, H. DUGMORE & RICO

MADAM!! -- DON'T OPEN THAT E-MAIL!! ¿GASP¿ TOO LATE!!

WHAT?! DON'T TELL ME -- THE MELISSA VIRUS?!!

THE DOMESTIC VIRUS! ¿CHOKE¿ ALREADY... I'M FEELING WEAK...

MUST BE SOMETHING NEW.

HELLO. I'M VUSI MAHALA, COMPUTER VIRUS SPECIALIST. I CAME AS SOON AS I COULD.

THANK GOODNESS! YOUR PHONE NUMBER WAS ALREADY ON THE SCREEN.

WHAT SEEMS TO BE THE PROBLEM?

IT'S OUR MAID. I OPENED UP AN UNSOLICITATED E-MAIL BY MISTAKE.

LET'S SEE... LOW ENERGY... MEMORY LOSS... SHE SEEMS TO HAVE TOTALLY **SHUT DOWN.**

HMMM... JUST AS I THOUGHT. IT'S THE **DOMESTIC VIRUS,** ALRIGHT. HALF THE MAIDS IN THIS SUBURB HAVE ALREADY CRASHED.

TIC TIC TIC TIC TIC TIC TIC

CAN'T YOU JUST... "RE-BOOT" HER OR SOMETHING?

IT'S TOO LATE FOR THAT. AS I'M SURE YOU'RE AWARE, YOUR RAM IS INCOMPATIBLE WITH YOUR MICROPROCESSOR'S ROOT DIRECTORY, CAUSING SEVERE MODEM AND LAN NETWORK INSTABILITY.

WHAT CAN WE DO?

LET THE VIRUS WORK ITSELF OUT. UNDER **NO** CIRCUMSTANCES IS YOUR MAID TO **WORK** FOR THE NEXT TWO WEEKS.

I'M SORRY -- BUT I MUST LEAVE. THIS "DOMESTIC VIRUS" IS PARTICULARLY NASTY. MANY OTHERS MAY NEED MY HELP.

WE UNDERSTAND COMPLETELY.

IT ALWAYS AMAZES ME HOW SOMEONE CAN OWN A COMPUTER AND HAVE **NO IDEA** HOW IT ACTUALLY WORKS.

THANKS, COUSIN VUSI. SAY HI TO AUNT VIOLET.

HI--THIS IS DAN...AND I'M PIET...AND WE'RE REPORTING **LIVE** ON **JAY NAIDOO'S** HISTORIC 21-DAY TELECOMMUNICATIONS ROAD RALLY ACROSS THE AFRICAN CONTINENT.

THAT'S RIGHT, PIET. BEGINNING IN SUN-DRENCHED **TUNISIA**, JAY WILL PERSON-ALLY DRIVE OVER **750 KM'S A DAY** -- BRINGING A MESSAGE OF **HOPE** AND **TELECOMMUNICATIONS** TO THE PEOPLE OF AFRICA.

IF I MAY ASK, JAY -- A "TELECOMMUNICATIONS ROAD RALLY" TEN WEEKS BE-FORE THE ELECTIONS? WHOSE IDEA **WAS** THIS?

I DON'T KNOW, DAN. BUT WHEN I **FIND OUT**, I'M GOING TO...

HEE-HEE!   HAW-HAW!

HOO-HOO!

:CHUCKLE:

PIET AND DAN HERE... CONTINUING OUR **LIVE** COVERAGE OF **JAY NAIDOO'S** HISTORIC 21-DAY TELE-COMMUNICATIONS CAR RALLY ACROSS THE AFRICAN CONTINENT.

AS YOU CAN SEE, JAY HAS STOPPED HIS CAR TO ADDRESS A GROUP OF LOCALS.

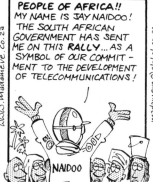

PEOPLE OF AFRICA!! MY NAME IS JAY NAIDOO! THE SOUTH AFRICAN GOVERNMENT HAS SENT ME ON THIS **RALLY**... AS A SYMBOL OF OUR COMMIT-MENT TO THE DEVELOPMENT OF TELECOMMUNICATIONS!

ANY QUESTIONS?

YES. WHEN CAN WE EXPECT THE RUNNING WATER HOUSING, OR EMPLOYMENT CAR RALLY?

We are currently experiencing technical difficulties. We apologise for any inconvenience.

THIS IS DAN AND PIET... ONCE AGAIN REPORTING **LIVE** FROM THE HISTORIC **JAY NAIDOO** TELE-COMMUNICATIONS CAR RALLY... WHERE JAY NAIDOO WILL PERSONALLY **DRIVE** FOR 21 DAYS IN THE HOT AFRICAN SUN ACROSS THE CONTINENT, HIGHLIGHTING THE IMPORTANCE OF TELE-COMMUNICATIONS TO THE PEOPLE OF AFRICA.

JAY, SOME CRITICS MIGHT SUGGEST THAT THIS "RALLY" IS ACTUALLY A **SILLY NON-EVENT** ENGINEERED BY YOUR POLITICAL ENEMIES. HOW DO YOU RESPOND TO THAT?

TYPICAL MEDIA! RUMOUR... GOSSIP AND INNUENDO.

THIS IS A VERY SERIOUS...

OKAY!! WHO PUT THOSE SMILEY FACE BALLOONS ON MY RALLY CAR?!

HEE HEE!

HOO-HOO!

:CHUCKLE:

HI, PIET AND DAN HERE... WITH OUR CONTINUED *LIVE* COVERAGE OF **JAY NAIDOO'S** HISTORIC 11 NATION, 21-DAY **TELECOMMUNICATIONS ROAD RALLY** ACROSS THE AFRICAN CONTINENT...

...UNFORTUNATELY THE RALLY **HAS** HAD A MINOR SET-BACK TODAY. AT APPROXIMATELY 11H03 AM LOCAL TIME OUR TWO RALLY CARS WERE MERCILESSLY **HIJACKED** BY UNKNOWN ASSAILANTS.

...WE'D CALL FOR HELP, BUT UNFORTUNATELY NONE OF OUR CELLPHONES SEEM TO BE WORKING IN THIS AREA ...

SOB

SO IF ANYONE IS WATCHING THIS BROADCAST, PLEASE SEND HELP. WE'RE SOMEWHERE NORTH OF OUAGADOUGOU, NEXT TO A HERD OF CAMELS...

HI. PIET AND DAN HERE... WITH A SPECIAL REPORT ON **JAY NAIDOO'S** HISTORIC CROSS-CONTINENTAL **TELECOMMUNICATIONS ROAD RALLY.**

THAT'S RIGHT, PIET. IN FACT, JAY NAIDOO'S RALLY HAS BEEN SO **SUCCESSFUL** ... THAT OTHER POLITICIANS ARE ALREADY PLANNING THEIR **OWN SPORTS EVENTS** IN AN EFFORT TO BEEF UP THEIR POLITICAL PROFILES.

SOME OF THE UPCOMING EVENTS ALREADY ANNOUNCED INCLUDE THE "ALFRED NZO FOREIGN AFFAIRS CHESS TOURNAMENT."...

THE "CHIEF BUTHELEZI COAST TO COAST BUNGI JUMP JAMBOREE"...

THE "TONY LEON HOT AIR BALLOON TRIATHLON"...

AND THIS JUST IN... THE "WINNIE MANDELA FULL CONTACT AMATEUR SOCCER KNOCK-OUT CUP."

VIVA GWEN ANDERSON, VIVA!

VIVA EDITH ANDERSON, VIVA!

VIVA THE ENTIRE ANDERSON HOUSE-HOLD, VIVA!!

VIVA ALL MADAMS IN GENERAL, VIVA!!

LET ME GUESS. IT'S WAGE NEGOTIATION TIME.

VIVA GWEN ANDERSON, VIVA!!

KEEP IT UP. YOU'RE STILL NOT GETTING A RAISE.

WHAT'S WITH THIS "VIVA" THING?

IN BLACK CULTURE "VIVA" IS AN EXPRESSION OF PRAISE AND ACKNOWLEDGEMENT.

THAT'S ALL THERE IS TO IT?

GO AHEAD. TRY IT OUT FOR YOURSELF.

VIVA ANOTHER GIN & TONIC, VIVA!

CLOSE.

LET ME GET THIS STRAIGHT. "VIVA" IS AN EXPRESSION OF PRAISE OR ACKNOWLEDGEMENT.

YOU'VE BEEN IN THIS COUNTRY ALL THESE YEARS AND YOU DIDN'T KNOW THAT?!

WHAT DID YOU THINK "VIVA" MEANT?

I NEVER GAVE IT MUCH THOUGHT. ...A CAR?

"THE 1999 VIVA". ...HAS A NICE RING TO IT.

MAYBE WE COULD SELL IT TO VOLKSWAGEN.

MADAM & Eve

BY S. FRANCIS, H. DUGMORE & RICO

I'LL VOTE FOR WHOEVER YOU WANT
Only 10 Rand

CONSIDER ME A FREE-LANCE LOBBYIST.

I'LL VOTE FOR WHOEVER YOU WANT
Only 10 Rand

SO LET ME GET THIS STRAIGHT. I PAY YOU TEN BUCKS...AND THEN YOU'LL VOTE FOR ANYONE I TELL YOU TO?

YEBO.

I'LL VOTE FOR WHOEVER YOU WANT

FOR TEN BUCKS, WOULD YOU VOTE FOR THE ANC OR THE NNP?

YEP.

I'LL VOTE FOR WHOEVER YOU WANT
Only 10 Rand

WOULD YOU VOTE FOR THE UDM OR THE DP?

YEP.

I'LL VOTE FOR

WHAT ABOUT THE IFP?

LOUIS LUYT?

THE PAC?

YEP.

YEP.

YEP.

I'LL VOTE FOR WHOEVER

©RAPID PHASE - 1999

WHAT ABOUT ME? WOULD YOU VOTE FOR ME?

I'LL VOT FOR

I'LL VOT FOR

WAIT A MINUTE. YOU'RE SAYING -- HYPOTHETICALLY, YOU WOULDN'T VOTE FOR ME -- EVEN FOR TEN BUCKS?!!

I'LL VOTE FOR WHOEVER

FINE! FORGET THE WHOLE THING!

I'LL VOTE FOR WHOEVER

www.madamandeve.co.za

SOONER OR LATER, EVERYONE HAS A LINE THEY WON'T CROSS.

I'LL VOTE FOR WHOEVER

:GASP:

ARE.. ARE.. ARE.. YOU WHO I **THINK** YOU ARE?

YES. BUT DON'T WORRY. I HAVEN'T COME FOR YOU OR ANYONE YOU KNOW.

THEN WHY COME TO **MY** HOUSE?

ACTUALLY, I HAVE SOME TIME TO KILL. I'M DUE AT A HIJACKING UP THE STREET IN FORTY MINUTES.

GOT A LIGHT?

THOSE THINGS WILL KILL YOU.

"DEATH" VISITS THE SUBURBS...

I CAN'T **BELIEVE** I'M SITTING NEXT TO **DEATH**.

YEP.

... ACTUALLY, I GO BY MANY NAMES: "THE GRIM REAPER"... "DEATH"..."THE BIG SLEEP"... ... "MR ETERNITY"...

SO...ER, WHAT SHOULD I CALL YOU?

JUST CALL ME BOB.

"BOB"??? ...BOB DEATH?!

SO. ANYTHING GOOD ON TV?

"DEATH" VISITS MOTHER ANDERSON...

SO. YOU LIKE SOUTH AFRICA?

ABSOLUTELY **LOVE** IT. BUSY, BUSY, BUSY.

ALTHOUGH LATELY, I **HAVE** BEEN THINKING OF EMIGRATING.

HEE-HEE. I'M **JOKING**, OF COURSE.

THIS "DEATH" IS A MORON.

BY THE WAY, I CAN READ YOUR MIND.

"DEATH" TAKES A HOLIDAY...

I LOST MY **KEYS** LAST MONTH. SINCE YOU KNOW **EVERYTHING** THAT HAPPENS IN THE **UNIVERSE** --

THEY FELL DOWN THE SEAT IN YOUR CAR. LOOK THERE.

WOW. TELL ME MORE OF THE UNKNOWN!

≤SIGH≥ TRUST ME. SOME THINGS YOU WOULDN'T **WANT** TO **KNOW.**

OH, COME ON!

OKAY. WHILE YOU WERE ASLEEP LAST NIGHT, YOU SWALLOWED A BIG **BUG.**

... AND REMEMBER THAT CORNISH PIE YOU ATE AT THE CORNER CAFE LAST WEEK? IT WAS MADE WITH --

OKAY! OKAY!

TELL ME THE TRUTH. WHAT DOES "DEATH" REALLY LOOK LIKE?

YOU WANT TO SEE MY FACE?

≤GASP≥ YOU'RE **BLACK?!!**

JUST KIDDING -- ACTUALLY, I HAVE THE POWER TO LOOK LIKE **ANYONE** I WANT! IT'S A BIG HIT AT DINNER PARTIES.

OKAY -- WHO'S THIS? **EVE! WHERE'S MY GIN & TONIC?!**

VERY FUNNY.

"DEATH" TAKES A HOLIDAY...

GOT ANY BILTONG?

YOU EAT **FOOD?!**

JUST BECAUSE I'M **DEATH,** THAT DOESN'T MEAN I DON'T GET HUNGRY OR TIRED!

YOU GET **TIRED** TOO?!

HEY -- YOU KNOW HOW MUCH **WALKING** I HAVE TO DO EVERY DAY?!!

THANK GOODNESS FOR REEBOKS.

THOSE ARE NIKES.

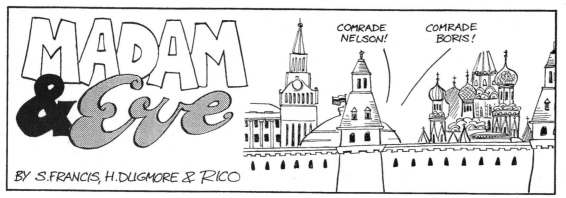

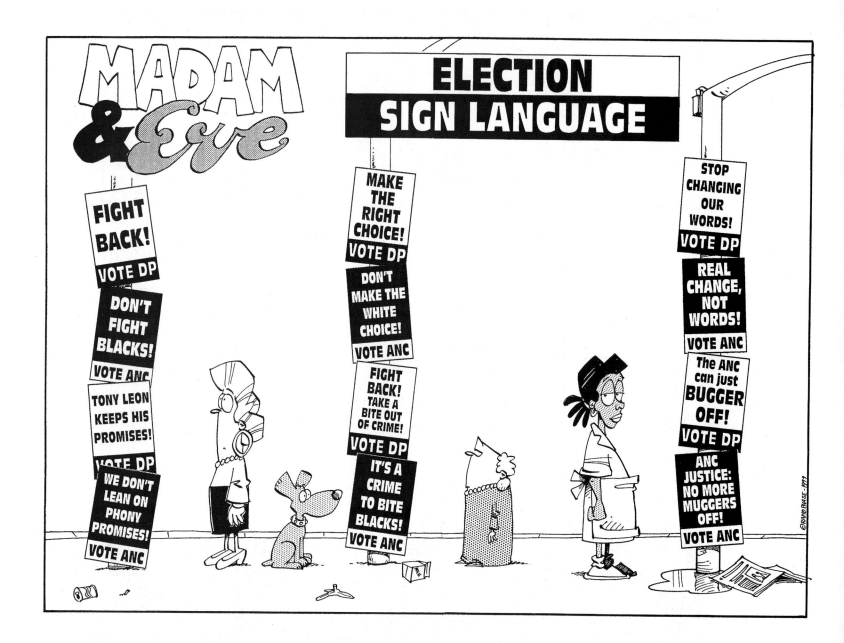

MRS. ANDERSON-- IF ELECTED, WHAT WILL THE "SURPRISE PARTY" DO FOR THE COUNTRY?

VOTE FOR THE SURPRISE PARTY

THAT'S THE SURPRISE!! ...WILL WE WORK FOR HOUSING AND JOB CREATION... OR MERELY ENRICH OUR- SELVES AT TAXPAYER'S EXPENSE??...EVEN WE DON'T KNOW!!

VOTE FOR

SO ROLL THE DICE AND VOTE FOR "THE SURPRISE PARTY". ...WHAT HAVE YOU GOT TO LOSE?!

VOTE FOR

...ER, OUR DEMOCRACY?

OH, COME ON! WHERE'S YOUR SENSE OF ADVENTURE?!

©RARD PHASE- 1999   WWW.MADBONEVE.CO.ZA

AS PROMISED, I WOULD NOW LIKE TO INTRODUCE THE LEADER OF "THE SURPRISE PARTY".

VOTE FOR THE SURPRISE PARTY

COULD YOU TELL US HIS OR HER NAME?

OF COURSE NOT! I DON'T WANT TO SPOIL THE SURPRISE.

VOTE FOR

COULD YOU AT LEAST TELL US IF HE OR SHE HAS ANY LEADER- SHIP EXPERIENCE?

SORRY. THAT'S ALSO A SURPRISE. YOU'LL JUST HAVE TO WAIT.

VOTE FOR

THE MEDIA. THEY JUST DON'T KNOW WHEN TO STOP.

VOTE FOR

MADAM & Eve

BY S. FRANCIS, H. DUGMORE & RICO

MADAM... I NEED TO TAKE TOMORROW OFF. MY UNCLE JOE JUST DIED.

ACCORDING TO MY RECORDS, YOUR UNCLE JOE DIED LAST FEBRUARY.

DID I SAY UNCLE JOE? I MEANT UNCLE MOE.

LET'S BE DEMOCRATIC. WE'LL PUT IT TO A VOTE.

HEAR, HEAR.

ALL THOSE IN FAVOUR OF EVE TAKING TOMORROW OFF, RAISE YOUR HAND.

SORRY. YOU LOSE.

MADAM... I HAVE A **RIGHT** TO TAKE DAYS OFF. IT'S IN MY **EMPLOYMENT CONTRACT.**

FINE. ALL THOSE IN FAVOUR OF **CHANGING** EVE'S EMPLOYMENT CONTRACT, RAISE YOUR HAND.

MOTION CARRIED.

THIS ISN'T **FAIR.** YOU HAVE A **TWO-THIRDS MAJORITY.**

AHA!! TWO-THIRDS MAJORITY! TWO-THIRDS MAJORITY!!

YOU **SEE**?!

I'LL REALLY BE GLAD WHEN THIS ELECTION'S OVER.

©RAPID PHASE - 1999

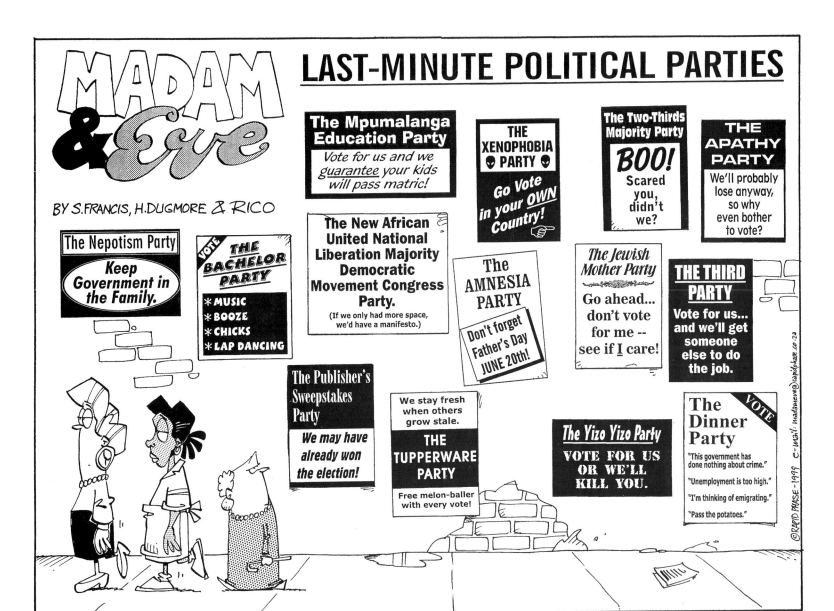

MORE COFFEE, MADAM?

LIFT YOUR FEET, PLEASE.

MORNING, MRS. ANDERSON.

I'VE DECIDED TO OUTSOURCE.

EVE! WHO ARE ALL THESE STRANGERS IN MY HOUSE? I TOLD YOU, I'VE DECIDED TO "OUTSOURCE".

ALL IT TAKES IS A LITTLE SUPERVISION, AND I HAVE LOTS MORE FREE TIME.

YOUR TEA, MADAM. WHY THANK YOU, PRECIOUS.

WAIT A MINUTE!! I'M MADAM, DAMMIT! PLEASE. YOU'RE SCARING MY SUB-CONTRACTORS.

ATTENTION ALL SUBCON-TRACTORS! HERE ARE THIS AFTERNOON'S ASSIGNMENTS: PRECIOUS--THE WINDOWS. JOE--TAKE THE KITCHEN. MARIA--DO THE WASHING.

AND WHAT DO YOU DO? I PROJECT-MANAGE, PROBLEM-SOLVE AND KEEP THEM GOAL ORIENTATED.

WHO GETS THE GIN & TONIC? SHE DOES.

...SEE?

©RAPID PHASE - 1999

e-mail: madameve@rapidphase.co.za

MADAM... I REPRESENT THE OTHER SUBCONTRACTORS. WE'VE TALKED AMONG OURSELVES... AND WE FEEL WE DESERVE AN INCREASE IN WAGES.

OH FINE!! I'LL GIVE YOU TEN PERCENT! NOW BACK TO WORK!!

©RAPID PHASE 1999

EMPLOYEES! ...YOU GIVE THEM A HAND AND THEY WANT THE WHOLE ARM!

COUGH COUGH COUGH

COUGH COUGH COUGH

WHAT?

www.madameve.co.za

EVE! WHAT'S GOING ON?! THE HOUSE STILL ISN'T CLEAN!!

I KNOW. I'M HAVING A SMALL "OUTSOURCING" CRISIS.

WHAT'S WRONG?

THE PEOPLE I SUBCONTRACTED TO, SUBCONTRACTED TO OTHER PEOPLE... AND THEY IN TURN, SUBCONTRACTED TO SOMEONE ELSE.

©RAPID PHASE-1999

SO NOW WHO'S CLEANING THE HOUSE?!

WE'RE DOWN TO A GROUP OF ILLEGAL IMMIGRANTS FROM BULGARIA. THEY WORK VERY CHEAP.

e-mail: madameve@rapidphase.co.za

PLEASE TO MOVE LEGS. AM NEEDING TO SUCK CARPET.

141

MISTER POWER... THABO MBEKI IS HERE FOR HIS APPOINTMENT.

GOOD. SEND HIM IN.

MISTER POWER...YOU'RE AN EXPERT ON MOTIVATION AND IMAGE. I NEED YOUR HELP.

GO ON.

PEOPLE SAY I'M AN ENIGMA... A CIPHER. NO ONE KNOWS WHAT I'M REALLY LIKE!

IN OTHER WORDS...

I NEED A PERSONALITY.

MARGE... HOLD MY CALLS. THIS COULD TAKE A WHILE.

OKAY, MISTER MBEKI, LET'S DO SOME VISUALISATION. IF YOU HAD A PERSONALITY... WHAT WOULD YOU LIKE IT TO BE?

I GUESS I'D LIKE TO BE A FUN GUY... TOUGH, BUT FAIR... THE LIFE OF THE PARTY... I MEAN THE ANC PARTY, OF COURSE.

OKAY. WE CAN BUILD ON THAT.

BUZZ

HOLD THAT THOUGHT.

MISTER POWER-- LOUIS LUYT'S ON THE LINE. HE FORGOT HIS HUMILITY EXERCISE.

I BETTER TAKE THIS.

MISTER MBEKI... IF I'M GOING TO HELP YOU, YOU'VE GOT TO STOP HIDING BEHIND RHETORIC AND LET PEOPLE SEE WHO YOU REALLY ARE!

I'M READY.

OKAY. TELL ME ABOUT YOURSELF. WHAT ARE YOUR LIKES? ...YOUR DISLIKES?

LET'S SEE.. I LIKE PINA COLADAS, GETTING CAUGHT IN THE RAIN, I AM NOT INTO YOGA, I AM INTO CHAMPAGNE.

THABO ...THAT'S A SONG.

PURE COINCIDENCE.

MADAM & EVE

BY S. FRANCIS, H. DUGMORE & RICO

DOCTOR...THE ANDERSONS ARE HERE TO SEE YOU.

GOOD. SEND THEM IN.

IT'S MY MOTHER, DOCTOR. SHE'S SUFFERING FROM P.E.S.T.

AH...POST ELECTION STRESS TRAUMA.

I'VE SEEN THIS BEFORE. ...SENSORY OVERLOAD DUE TO TOO MANY PROMISES, POLITICS AND POSTERS. WHEN DID THIS HAPPEN?

email: madameve@rapidphase.co.za

THIS MORNING. SHE WENT INTO A FOETAL POSITION AND BEGAN SHOUTING ELECTION SLOGANS!!

AAAAAAH!! THE ANC!! "A BETTER LIFE FOR ALL!! TOGETHER FOR CHANGE!"

www.madameve.co.za

AAAAAH!! CHIEF BUTHELEZI!! "MAKE THE COUNTRY GOVERNABLE AGAIN!"

MRS ANDERSON!! SNAP OUT OF IT!!

HUH?

I THINK SHE'S COMING OUT OF IT. WHATEVER YOU DO, DON'T EXPOSE HER TO ANYTHING TO DO WITH ELECTIONS OR SHE COULD GO BACK INTO A COMA.

© RAPID PHASE - 1999

W-WHERE AM I?

YOU CAN DO IT, MOM!! HAVE THE GUTS TO FIGHT BACK!!

AHHHH!! TONY LEON!!

OOPS.

BETTER LEAVE THIS TO THE PROFESSIONALS.

CELLPHONES FROM OUTER SPACE...

SURRENDER, EARTHLING. RESISTANCE IS FUTILE!

EVEN AS WE SPEAK, THOUSANDS OF US HAVE **INFILTRATED** YOUR SOCIETY... WAITING PATIENTLY TO **REVEAL** OUR PRESENCE.

DO YOU HAVE ANY **IDEA** WHAT IT WAS LIKE? FOR YEARS, HAVING TO REMAIN SILENT... BEING PRESSED AGAINST YOUR BIG EARS... LETTING YOU TALK INTO OUR STOMACHS...

EWWWWW!

EXACTLY.

IF YOU CELLPHONES **FROM OUTER SPACE** THINK YOU CAN ENSLAVE US YOU'RE NOT PLAYING WITH A FULL SIM CARD!

YOU LEAVE US, NO CHOICE. PUNY EARTHLINGS... PREPARE TO BE ZAPPED WITH OUR MICROWAVES!

ZAP!
ZAP!

HEY! MY TEA'S HOT!

WE NEED BETTER WEAPONS.

HI MOM. THIS IS MY NEW FRIEND, "JUSTICE".

HELLO JUSTICE.

HE'S ONE OF THE NEW BREED OF DISENCHANTED BLACK YOUTH. HE'S TURNED HIS BACK ON POLITICS AND THE TRADITIONAL LIFESTYLE OF HIS PARENTS.

KWAITO IS MY LIFE, MAN!

OH GOOD. THE MARTIAL ARTS.

FACE IT, MOM. THERE'S A WHOLE NEW GENERATION OUT THERE.

BOOM SHAKA ARE MY HEROES! THEIR MUSIC **SPEAKS** TO ME!

NOW DO YOU UNDERSTAND, MOM?

CERTAINLY! WHEN I WAS HIS AGE, **CLIFF RICHARD** SPOKE TO ME!

FREE! FROM THE CHAINS THAT ARE BINDING ME--

WE'RE ALL GOING ON A... SUMMER HOLIDAY!!

DON'T ASK.

MOM... JUSTICE MAY BE A MEMBER OF THE DISENCHANTED BLACK YOUTH OF TODAY... BUT HE'S NOT THAT DIFFERENT FROM YOU AND ME.

HE MAY NOT BE ABLE TO GET A JOB... BUT HE HAS THE SAME "WANTS" AS WE DO.

LIKE MONEY.

MONEY?

YES. YOU HAVE IT. I WANT IT.

COOL, HEY?

JUSTICE -- IF YOU'RE SERIOUS ABOUT FINDING A JOB... HERE'S ONE IN THE AUTOMOBILE INDUSTRY.

C-mail: madameve@rapidphase.co.za

THEY'D NEVER HIRE ME, MAN. I DON'T HAVE THE SKILLS.

HE'S BEING MODEST.

YESTERDAY, I ACCIDENTALLY LOCKED MY KEYS IN MY CAR... JUSTICE OPENED IT UP IN TWO SECONDS.

...AND YOU SHOULD SEE HOW FAST HE CAN REMOVE A CAR RADIO!

...AND THAT'S WITH JUST A WIRE HANGER.

©RAPID PHASE - 1999

THE TRUTH IS, MOM... JUSTICE AND I ARE THINKING OF FORMING A KWAITO BAND AND MAKING LOTS OF MONEY.

YO. CHECK IT OUT!

I DON'T GET IT. WHAT ARE YOU DOING?

www.madameve.co.za

IF WE EVER PUT OUT A CD, THAT'S THE COVER.

©RAPID PHASE - 1999

LADIES... WELCOME TO **MAID & MADAM COUNSELLING.** SIMILAR TO MARRIAGE COUNSELLING, YOU MUST NOT HESITATE TO BE **TRUTHFUL.**

OKAY, LET'S BEGIN. EVE... YOU GO FIRST. WHAT'S ONE OF YOUR BIGGEST COMPLAINTS?

WELL... I THINK MADAM IS CHEAP.

NO, EVE. IN COUNSELLING WE NEVER "THINK". WE ONLY DEAL WITH FEELINGS.

OKAY. I FEEL MADAM IS CHEAP.

GOOD!

BEFORE I BEGIN THE COUNSELLING, I'D LIKE YOU BOTH TO TAKE THIS **MAID & MADAM DOMESTIC TEST.** REMEMBER... THERE ARE NO "RIGHT" OR "WRONG" ANSWERS.

"QUESTION Nº 1: TRUE OR FALSE: IN MY HOUSE, THE MAID IS ALWAYS PAID A FAIR WAGE".

FALSE.   TRUE.

THIS IS EASY.

MADAM & MAID COUNSELLING...

QUESTION Nº 50: "WHAT DOES YOUR MAID OR MADAM DO THAT ANNOYS YOU MOST? MAKE A LIST.

CAN WE WRITE ON BOTH SIDES OF THE PAGE?

OF COURSE.

CAN I PLEASE HAVE A FEW MORE SHEETS OF PAPER?

CERTAINLY.

CAN WE TAKE A SHORT BREAK? I'M GETTING A CRAMP IN MY HA--

OH, GIVE IT A REST?!

MADAM & Eve

OUT DAMNED SPOT!!

BY S. FRANCIS, H. DUGMORE & RICO

PURPLE
ELECTION
INK
REMOVAL
Only 10 Rand

HERE'S TEN BUCKS. THIS WON'T **HURT**, WILL IT?

NOT REALLY. HOWEVER, YOU MIGHT EXPERIENCE SOME SLIGHT DISCOMFORT.

PURPLE ELECTION

RIGHT. GO AHEAD.

OKAY. LET'S GET READY. ... RAZOR BLADE.

...RAZOR BLADE.

HAND DRILL.

HAND DRILL

CHISEL.

CHISEL.

WOODEN HAMMER.

WOODEN HAMMER.

BANG!

BETTER GIVE ME THE **LARGE** WOODEN HAMMER!

NEVER MIND!! KEEP THE MONEY! JUST FORGET THE WHOLE THING!!

www.madamaneve.co.za

WAIT, COME BACK! YOU NEED TO SOAK YOUR THUMB IN BOILING PARAFFIN!!

PURPLE ELECTION INK REMOVAL
Only 10 Rand

...A PURPLE THUMB IS A SMALL PRICE TO PAY FOR DEMOCRACY.

YOU OWE ME FIVE BUCKS.

©RAPID PHASE - 1999

MADAM & Eve

BY S. FRANCIS, H. DUGMORE & RICO

WELCOME TO MY **STAR WARS PARTY!** ...WHO ARE YOU?

TRUST YOUR FEELINGS, LUKE. I AM ...YOUR MOTHER.

COOL!

...AND I BROUGHT EVE, MOM AND THANDI.

BREEP.

BEEP-BEEP! DJEEP-BIP! BIDDI-BEEP!

IRRITATING ME, YOU ARE.

COME IN EVERYBODY.

I CAN'T BELIEVE IT. MOTHER ANDERSON AS **YODA.**

I TOLD HER SHE SHOULD COME AS ONE OF THE NEW STAR WARS CHARACTERS... ..."QUI-GON GIN."

GET IT? "...QUI-GON **GIN.**"

QUIET YOU SHOULD BE IF SURVIVE YOU WANT TO.

THE BAR LOOKS PRETTY CROWDED, MOTHER ANDERSON. I'LL TRY AND GET YOU A DRINK.

EITHER DO... OR NO DO. THERE IS NO "TRY."

YOU KNOW...I ALWAYS WONDERED WHY, AFTER 800 YEARS, YODA STILL CAN'T SPEAK PROPERLY.

WASTING TIME YOU ARE. HEAD FOR THE BAR.

PRINCESS EVA! WHERE IS THE LOCATION OF THE REBEL BASE?

MADAMS. THEY CAN'T FIND ANYTHING.

ANY WHITE MEAT TURKEY LEFT?

NO. GO OVER TO THE DARK SIDE.

MAY THE FORK BE WITH YOU.

YOUR LUCK YOU ARE PUSHING.

STAR WARS
THE PHANTOM MENACE

I CAN'T BELIEVE IT, EVE. WHO IN THEIR RIGHT MIND WOULD ACTUALLY DRESS UP IN A COSTUME TO GO SEE A MOVIE?

CAST ADRIFT AND LOST AT SEA... NO WATER... THE CRUEL SUN UNRELENTING IN ITS SEARING HEAT.

BUT WHAT'S THIS?! A SHIP! I'M SAVED!!

AHOY THERE!!

WILL YOU STOP DAYDREAMING AND GET TO WORK?!!

JUST MY LUCK... IT WAS A SLAVE SHIP, RUN BY THE NEFARIOUS "CAPTAIN ANDERSON."

ATTENTION EVERYONE... I HAVE A BRIEF STATEMENT. NELSON MANDELA WISHES TO RETIRE QUIETLY AND LEAD A PRIVATE LIFE. HE HOPES YOU WILL RESPECT HIS WISHES.

AS A MATTER OF FACT, HE HAS ALREADY **LEFT** THE BUILDING.

FREE AT LAST.

NOW OUT OF POLITICS, NELSON MANDELA SEEMS TO HAVE DISAPPEARED FROM THE PUBLIC SPOT-LIGHT... ALLEGEDLY "RETIRING" TO THE VILLAGE OF HIS BIRTH.

NEVERTHELESS, THERE HAVE BEEN NUMEROUS "MANDELA SIGHTINGS" FROM CAPE TOWN TO BOKSBURG... AT SHOPPING MALLS, RAVES AND FAST FOOD RESTAURANTS.

THE QUESTION MANY SOUTH AFRICANS SEEM TO BE ASKING IS: "**WHERE** IS NELSON MANDELA... AND **WHAT** IS HE REALLY DOING?"

THAT'S **HIM** , I TELL YOU! ... OVER BY THE FROZEN PEAS!

THAT BEARD IS DEFINITELY PHONEY.

MEAT

I'M TELLING YOU THAT'S **HIM**! NELSON MANDELA RIGHT IN OUR SUPER-MARKET!

...WITH A **BEARD** ?

IT'S A **DISGUISE**! "RETIRING TO HIS HOME VILLAGE" WAS JUST A COVER STORY TO ESCAPE THE MEDIA.

SHHH. WHAT'S HE DOING?

TRYING TO GET HIS TROLLEY UNSTUCK.

FREE! AT LAST!!

CLANG

AHA!!

CANNED MIELIES

156

WELL, IT'S BEEN OVER A WEEK SINCE PRESIDENT THABO MBEKI APPOINTED **DOCTOR ZUMA** MINISTER OF FOREIGN AFFAIRS...

ALTHOUGH WHAT NEW, BOLD FOREIGN AFFAIRS INITIATIVES DOCTOR ZUMA IS TAKING IS NOT YET CLEAR...

HOWEVER, ANALYSTS SAY THEY EXPECT DOCTOR ZUMA TO TAKE AS STRONG AND INDEPENDENT A LINE IN FOREIGN AFFAIRS... AS SHE DID WHEN SHE WAS MINISTER OF HEALTH.

SARAFINA 3!!? I LOVE IT! THIS TIME ALL THE **WORLD'S** OUR STAGE.

PICTURE IT, DOCTOR Z.-- **THE SARAFINA 3 MILLENIUM WORLD TOUR!!**

LOTS OF SINGING... DANCING... ALL WITH AN **EDUCATIONAL MESSAGE** ABOUT **FOREIGN AFFAIRS!** ...WHICH IS?

"IF YOU HAVE AN **AFFAIR** WITH A **FOREIGNER,** ALWAYS USE A **CONDOM.**" I LIKE IT.

GOOD NEWS, DOCTOR Z. I'VE ALMOST FINISHED THE PROPOSED BUDGET FOR **SARAFINA 3.**

LET'S SEE... ACTORS... SCENERY... EXPENSES... MISCELLANEOUS...

TWO CARRY THE ONE... ROUND IT OFF TO THE NEAREST NUMBER... WHAT'S THE TOTAL?

14 MILLION! --JUST LIKE **SARAFINA 2!** WHOAH! TALK ABOUT COINCIDENCE!

MADAM & Eve

BY S. FRANCIS, H. DUGMORE & RICO

LADIES & GENTLEMEN... WE'VE CALLED THIS PRESS CONFERENCE TO REFUTE ALL PREVIOUS STATEMENTS. THE ANC WOULD LIKE TO STRESS THAT IT IS **NOT** ACCEPTABLE FOR POLITICIANS TO **LIE**.

NOT THAT ANYONE EVER SAID THAT. WHICH, IF THEY DID, WE TOTALLY DENY IT.

HOWEVER, TO SETTLE ANY CONTROVERSY, ALL POLITICIANS IN THIS GOVERNMENT HAVE VOLUNTARILY AGREED TO WEAR **THESE**... PORTABLE **LIE DETECTORS**.

SO, FROM NOW ON, IF, FOR SOME REASON A POLITICIAN **ACCIDENTALLY** UTTERS AN **UNTRUTH**... YOU'LL HEAR AN ALARM WHICH SOUNDS LIKE **THIS**:

BEEP BEEP BEEP

...IN OTHER WORDS, LADIES AND GENTLEMEN... YOU HAVE NOTHING TO FEAR FROM SOUTH AFRICAN POLITICIANS.

BEEP BEEP BEEP

BECAUSE WE BELIEVE IN A TRANSPARENT GOVERNMENT.

BEEP BEEP BEEP

OKAY--A SEMI-TRANSPARENT GOVERNMENT.

BEEP BEEP BEEP

MILDLY TRANSPARENT.

BEEP BEEP BEEP

ER,... SLIGHTLY OPAQUE!

AFTER ALL, WE GREATLY RESPECT THE MEDIA AND **WELCOME** THEIR CRITICISM.

BEEP BEEP BEEP

...YOU DON'T BOTHER US AT ALL.

BEEP BEEP BEEP

...WE'LL TOLERATE YOU AS BEST WE CAN.

BEEP BEEP BEEP

YOU'RE SCUM-SUCKING VULTURES!

HEY! THAT FELT **GOOD**! TELLING THE TRUTH ACTUALLY FEELS **GOOD**! ...ANY QUESTIONS?

YES? -- THE CHEAP-LOOKING JOURNALIST WITH THE BAD DYE JOB?

IS THAT YOU OR ME?

MADAM & EVE

BY S. FRANCIS, H. DUGMORE & RICO

HELLO. MY NAME IS GWEN.
I'M A MEMBER OF **ROAD RAGE ANONYMOUS**.

HI GWEN!!

AT FIRST I DIDN'T THINK I HAD A PROBLEM. EVERYBODY DID IT. YOU KNOW -- FLASHING YOUR HEADLIGHTS ... OR HOOTING WHEN THE ROBOT'S TURNED GREEN.

UH-HUH.

AND THEN, ONE DAY... I TRIED... **TAILGAITING**.

GASP!   GASP!!

AFTER THAT I COULDN'T STOP. I BEGAN **SHOUTING** AND **SWEARING** AT OTHER MOTORISTS... EVEN USING OBSCENE FINGER-SIGNS AT TAXIS.

WE'VE BEEN THERE!   TELL IT GIRL!

...BUT THE **ONE** THING THAT REALLY SET ME OFF -- THE **ONE THING** THAT WOULD ALWAYS DRIVE ME INTO AN **UNCONTROLLABLE RAGE**...

...IS WHEN SOMEBODY TOOK MY PARKING SPACE.

BY THE WAY. WHO OWNS A BLUE VOLKSWAGEN GOLF?

UH, I DO.

YOU SON OF A G@#G@!! YOU'RE IN MY SPACE!!

AND SHE WAS DOING SO WELL, TOO.   LEFT HOOK, GWEN!!

THAT WAS MY PARKING SPACE, YOU @✱#✶@!! / OH YEAH?! @#✶# YOU!!

LADIES... I USED TO SUFFER FROM ROAD RAGE TOO! ALL YOU HAVE TO DO IS TAKE TEN SECONDS... AND SLOWLY CALM DOWN.

©RAPID PHASE-1999 WWW.madameve.co.za

SEE?

©RAPID PHASE-1999

@#✶@!! WHO ASKED YOU?! / MIND YOUR OWN #✶@#✶ BUSINESS!!

I'M PROUD OF YOU, MADAM. IT'S BEEN FIVE DAYS... AND NOT ONCE HAVE YOU GIVEN IN TO ROAD RAGE.

©RAPID PHASE-1999 WWW. madameve.co.za

UH-OH.

DEEP BREATHS! --TAKE DEEP BREATHS!

OKAY. NOW SUDDENLY PULL OVER AND CHANGE LANES WITHOUT WARNING!

NO, NO! **DON'T** PUT ON YOUR INDICATOR! **NEVER** PUT ON YOUR INDICATOR!!

NOW -- **SLAM** ON THE BRAKES, WHISTLE AT THE WOMEN PEDESTRIANS AND BLOCK THE TRAFFIC!

GOOD! GOOD! YOU'RE DOING FINE!!

EVE SISULU'S MINIBUS TAXI DRIVING ACADEMY

Registration →

HERE'S MY TUITION FEE, Ms SISULU. I CAN'T **WAIT** TO BEGIN MY CAREER AS A HIGHLY PAID MINIBUS TAXI DRIVER!

SAY CHEESE.

CLICK.

WOW. MY FIRST FRAUDULENT DRIVER'S LICENSE.

EXCITING, ISN'T IT?

EVE'S MINIBUS TAXI SCHOOL

HERE'S YOUR FIRST LESSON, ...IN FRONT OF YOU IS THE MOST **IMPORTANT** THING FOR ALL MINIBUS TAXI DRIVERS...THEY CAN'T OPERATE WITHOUT IT.

...THE STEERING WHEEL?

NO.

THE REARVIEW MIRROR?

NO.

THE GEAR LEVER?

NO.

THE HOOTER!! FEEL THE POWER!!

BEEP! BEEP! BEEP! BEEP! BEEP!

EVE'S MINIBUS TAXI SCHOOL

OKAY... LET'S START WITH THE BASICS. YOU'RE DRIVING IN TRAFFIC WHEN YOU NOTICE TWO POTENTIAL PASSENGERS ON THE SIDE OF THE ROAD. **HOW** DO YOU GET TO THEM?

I PUT ON MY INDICATOR... I WAIT PATIENTLY FOR AN OPENING... THEN POLITELY CHANGE LANES, WAVING COURTEOUSLY TO THE MOTORIST BEHIND ME...

"THANK YOU FOR LETTING ME IN, SIR. I REALLY APPRECIATE IT!"

...WHAT?

©RAPID PHASE - 1999

EVE'S MINIBUS TAXI SCHOOL...

CONGRATULATIONS, VUSI. YOU'VE **PASSED** YOUR MINIBUS TAXI DRIVER TEST. NOW REPEAT AFTER ME: "I, VUSI MALABANE..."

I, VUSI MALABANE...

...PROMISE TO UPHOLD THE TRADITIONS OF TAXI DRIVERS EVERYWHERE, TO DRIVE **HOW-EVER** I WANT, **WHEREVER** I WANT, TO STOP **WHENEVER** I FEEL LIKE... TO **NEVER** INDICATE, ALWAYS **FLIRT** WITH WOMEN PEDESTRIANS AND **HOOT** CONSTANTLY.

...AS LONG AS MY PETROL TANK IS FULL, MY TYRES ARE BALD AND MY TAXI OVERLOADED... AS I DRIVE THROUGH A FREE AND DEMOCRATIC SOUTH AFRICA.

©RAPID PHASE - 1999

:CHOKE: THAT'S... BEAUTI-FUL.

HERE'S YOUR **DIPLOMA** AND COMPLIMENTARY BUMPER STICKER. NOW GO OUT THERE AND MAKE ME PROUD.

...AND IN OTHER NEWS, MORE ON THE TULI BABY ELEPHANT SCANDAL.

ACCORDING TO REPORTS, SEVERAL OF THE ABUSED YOUNG ELEPHANTS WERE RESCUED BY UNKNOWN ANIMAL RIGHTS ACTIVISTS.

NOBODY KNOWS WHERE THE ELEPHANTS ARE BEING HIDDEN, BUT AUTHORITIES ARE HOPING TO LOCATE THEM SOON...

THAT'S ODD. I COULD SWEAR I JUST FILLED UP MY GLASS WITH GIN & TONIC.

CAN YOU BELIEVE IT, EVE? THE AUTHORITIES BELIEVE THAT THE RESCUED TULI BABY ELEPHANT COULD BE HIDING SOMEWHERE IN THIS NEIGHBOURHOOD.

FWEEP

KA-SPLORTCH!!

GESUNDHEIT.   THANK YOU.

...AND IN OTHER NEWS, THE SEARCH CONTINUES FOR THE MISSING BABY ELEPHANT RESCUED LAST WEEK BY AN UNKNOWN ANIMAL RIGHTS ACTIVIST.

SNIFF SNIFF

HEY! WATCH WHERE YOU PUT THAT VACUUM!   SORRY.

I DON'T KNOW HOW MUCH LONGER I CAN KEEP THIS UP.

166

MADAM & Eve

GUNS 'R' US

BY S. FRANCIS, H. DUGMORE & RICO

HI. I'D LIKE TO BUY THIS KATTY.

FINE. HOWEVER, NEW LEGISLATION REQUIRES ALL NEW WEAPON OWNERS TO FIRST TAKE A **PSYCHOMETRIC TEST** TO ESTABLISH THEIR MENTAL CAPACITY TO HANDLE A DANGEROUS WEAPON.

WILL IT TAKE LONG? I'M IN A HURRY.

HMMM. "IMPATIENT AND TENSE"... NOT A GOOD SIGN.

ON SPECIAL

HEY! NOBODY TOLD ME THE TEST ALREADY **STARTED!**

OH... I SUPPOSE I "TRICKED" YOU -- IS THAT IT?! ...MAYBE YOU THINK I'M NOT BEING "FAIR."

NO. I, UH...

OKAY. OKAY. YOU'RE RIGHT. MAYBE WE GOT OFF ON THE WRONG FOOT. LET'S **SHAKE.**

WHOOOPS! TOO LATE. ...SUCKER!!

SAY... IS THAT YOUR **NOSE** OR ARE YOU EATING A **BANANA**?!

WHAT DID YOU SAY?!!

OH, RELAX. DON'T GET SO UPSET! HERE -- HAVE A ROSE.

OOOPS! THE OLD "SQUIRTING FLOWER TRICK"... AND YOU FELL FOR IT!!

SPLURT!!

ARE YOU CRAZY?!!

HELP! HELP! SECURITY!!

LET'S GO, MA'AM.

...AND TO THINK I ALMOST SOLD HER A KATTY.

MADAM & Eve

BY S. FRANCIS, H. DUGMORE & RICO

"TO BE ANNOUNCED." WHAT'S THAT MEAN?

IT MEANS I'M ABOUT TO OPEN A SUCCESSFUL NEW BUSINESS... I JUST DON'T KNOW WHAT IT IS YET.

HOW CAN YOU HAVE A BUSINESS AND NOT KNOW WHAT IT IS?!

DON'T BE SO IMPATIENT.

FIRST I HAVE TO ANALYSE THE MARKETPLACE...

...THEN, BY LOCATING A NICHE, I FAST-TRACK A SOLUTION AND DELIVER A VALUE-ADDED PRODUCT AT A REASONABLE PRICE.

WAIT A MINUTE -- I'M GETTING SOMETHING... IT'S COMING TO ME...

...YES! OF COURSE!! THAT'S IT! THAT'S MY NEW BUSINESS!!

(((RUMBLE)))

169

MADAM & Eve

SCARY HALLOWEEN MOVIES FOR SOUTH AFRICA

BY S. FRANCIS, H. DUGMORE & RICO

THE McBRIDE OF FRANKENSTEIN

HE SMUGGLED ILLEGAL ARMS... AND LEGS... AND FEET!

PSYCHO 3

THE HORROR, THE HORROR!

STARRING EUGENE DE KOCK DIRK COETZEE and CRAIG WILLIAMSON

VLAKPLAAS MOTEL

NIGHTMARE ON ELOFF STREET

DO YOU DARE DRIVE THRU?!

ONE, TWO, ROBBERS COMING FOR YOU.

THREE, FOUR, BETTER LOCK YOUR DOOR!

SMASH CRASH! YOU'VE GOT BROKEN GLASS!

THE CREATURE FROM THE BLACK CONSCIOUSNESS LAGOON

STALKING THE UNIVERSITIES... POLARISING EVERYONE!

Starring: Prof. William Makgoba

WIT WEREWOLF OF LONDON

WHEN THE MOON'S FULL... MONSTERS WALK THE STREETS!

©RARD PHASE - 1998

GODZUMA

UNSTOPPABLE! INDESTRUCTIBLE!

TOBACCO INDUSTRY

MILLIONS OF RANDS IN THE MAKING!

SIZE DOESN'T MATTER!

MARCH 23rd, WE SET OUT IN THE EARLY MORNING WITH A FEW SUPPLIES...

AFTER TRAVERSING TREACHEROUS MOUNTAIN TERRAIN, ONE OF OUR GUIDES BECAME EXCITED.

...FRESH SPOOR. WE KNEW WE WERE CLOSE.

WERE THE LEGENDS TRUE? DID THEY REALLY EXIST?

YES, SOON I WOULD COME FACE TO FACE WITH...

MADAMS IN THE MIST

TO BE CONTINUED...

GWEN... **WHAT** ARE YOU DOING WITH THAT FEATHER DUSTER?

WHAT DOES IT **LOOK** LIKE I'M DOING? I'M **CLEANING** UP!

AND NEVER MIND **ME**! WHAT ARE **YOU** DOING WITH THAT MOP AND BUCKET??

Panel 1: LOOK AT THIS BOOK I FOUND IN EVE'S ROOM. "HYPNOSIS MADE EASY." ...SO??

Panel 2: DON'T YOU GET IT? THIS EXPLAINS EVERYTHING! — LIKE WHAT?

Panel 3: LIKE OUR LAPSES OF MEMORY.. OR THE FACT THAT WE UNEXPLAINABLY FIND OURSELVES DOING HOUSEWORK. — WE DO?

Panel 4: COULD YOU PUT DOWN THAT IRON WHILE I'M TALKING TO YOU?!! — OH GOOD. I SEE YOU MADE LUNCH.

Panel 5: I'M NOT POSITIVE, MOM... BUT I THINK EVE HAS BEEN HYPNOTISING US INTO DOING ALL HER WORK. — SHE HAS?

Panel 6: THINK ABOUT IT! YESTERDAY I WOKE UP.. AND I WAS WASHING THE DISHES! — YOU'RE RIGHT! WHEN I WOKE UP, I WAS HOLDING A FEATHER DUSTER!!

Panel 7: I'M TELLING YOU... SOMETHING STRANGE IS DEFINITELY GOING ON HERE. — I AGREE.

Panel 8: HEY. NO TALKING DURING MY FOOT MASSAGE! — SHHH. WE'LL DISCUSS THIS LATER. — RIGHT. MUM'S THE WORD.

Panel 9: NICE TRY, EVE. BUT WE'RE WISE TO YOUR TRICKS! — THAT'S RIGHT! YOU'VE BEEN HYPNOTISING US!

Panel 10: WELL IT ALL STOPS NOW, MISSY! — THAT'S RIGHT! WHAT HAVE YOU GOT TO SAY FOR YOURSELF?!

Panel 11: SLEEP. — SNAP!

Panel 12: NEVER FAILS. AS SOON AS I SIT DOWN TO WATCH TV, THEY INTERRUPT ME.

APRIL 10th, OUR EFFORTS ARE REWARDED. AFTER WEEKS OF SEARCHING, WE HAVE FINALLY FOUND THE MADAMS IN THE MIST.

I ATTEMPT TO COMMUNICATE, USING SIMPLE HAND-SIGNALS.

ALTHOUGH WE MUST SEEM STRANGE TO THEM, I FEEL THEY ARE CONVINCED WE POSE NO THREAT OR DANGER.

INCREDIBLY, ONE OF THEM HANDS ME A CRUDE FEATHER DUSTER.

THEY APPEAR TO WANT ME TO **DO** SOMETHING WITH IT... BUT <u>WHAT</u>?!

HI THERE. I COME IN PEACE.

WE TOKOLOSHES AREN'T AS BAD AS PEOPLE THINK! WE'RE **VICTIMS** OF MISUNDERSTANDING AND PREJUDICE! WE'RE READY TO RECONCILE WITH SOUTH AFRICANS EVERYWHERE!

PICTURE IT... A **NEW** RAINBOW NATION. TOKOLOSHES... AND HUMANS... LIVING TOGETHER IN RACIAL HARMONY.

ARE YOU CRAZY?! YOU CARRY PEOPLE AWAY AT NIGHT AND THEY'RE NEVER SEEN AGAIN!!

HEY— NOBODY'S PERFECT.

THE TOKOLOSHES WANT TO RECONCILE WITH ALL HUMANITY.

WHAT?!

SURE... WE MAY LOOK DIFFERENT FROM YOU. WE HAVE PURPLE SKIN... AND LONG, POINTY TAILS. BUT INSIDE... WE'RE ALL THE SAME!

IF YOU PRICK US... DO WE NOT BLEED? IF YOU TICKLE US...DO WE NOT LAUGH? IF YOU POISON US...DO WE NOT DIE? TOKOLOSHES ARE PEOPLE TOO!

WHY CAN'T WE ALL JUST... GET ALONG?!

:SNIFF:

HE'S RIGHT, DAMMIT!

TOKOLOSHE TRUTH AND RECONCILIATION...

LET'S BEGIN.

OKAY. WHAT DO YOU WANT TO KNOW?

TWO YEARS AGO MY AUNT PALESA DISAPPEARED. SOME PEOPLE SAY SHE RAN AWAY WITH HER BOY-FRIEND... OTHERS SAY SHE WAS CARRIED OFF BY TOKOLOSHES.

Bzzzt.
Bzzzt.
Bzzzt.

AUNT PALESA: STOCKY... BIG-BONED... WEARS GLASSES?

UH-OH.

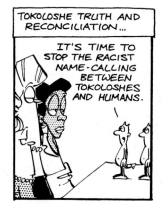

TOKOLOSHE TRUTH AND RECONCILIATION...

IT'S TIME TO STOP THE RACIST NAME-CALLING BETWEEN TOKOLOSHES AND HUMANS.

BEHIND OUR BACKS, YOU CALL US "MONSTERS", "DEVILS"... AND "DEMONS".

WE'RE SORRY.

THAT'S OKAY. WE CALL YOU "BRICK-HEADS", "TAKE-AWAYS", AND "BLANKET-BAIT".

..TAKE-AWAYS?!

HEY, IT'S GOOD TO GET THESE THINGS OUT IN THE OPEN.